Blame It on the Weather

Blame It on the Weather

STRANGE CANADIAN WEATHER FACTS

David Phillips

KEY PORTER BOOKS

Canadian Cataloguing in Publication Data

Phillips, David, 1944
  Blame it on the weather

Includes index.
ISBN 1-55013-968-1

1. Meteorology — Miscellanea. 2. Weather — Miscellanea. I. Title.

QC861.2.P44 1998   551.5   C98-930010-2

The Canada Council | Le Conseil des Arts
for the Arts | du Canada
since 1957 | depuis 1957

The publisher gratefully acknowledges the support of the Canada Council for the Arts and the Ontario Arts Council for its publishing program.
We acknowledge the financial support of the Government of Canada through the Book Publishing Industry Development Program for our publishing activities.

Key Porter Books Limited
70 The Esplanade
Toronto, Ontario
Canada M5E 1R2

www.keyporter.com

Design: Peter Maher
Electronic formatting: Niche Electronic Publishing

Printed and bound in Canada

98 99 00 01   6 5 4 3 2 1

Contents

Weatherwise

Plumes of exhaust blend with ice fog, shrouding Fort McMurray, Alberta, in a cold haze. *John Kenney/Canapress.*

LIVING WITH
PINATUBO'S FALLOUT

Since the fiery eruption of Mount Pinatubo in the Philippines in June 1991, the weather in many parts of the world has taken an unusual turn. Global temperatures in 1992 and 1993 fell below the record warm levels of the 1980s—a phenomenon many climatologists attribute to the large amounts of gases and ash that Pinatubo propelled into the atmosphere.

After 635 years of dormancy, Pinatubo erupted with a blast equated to 2,500 Hiroshima bombs. The volcano spewed a plume of grey ash, fiery debris and hot gases 40 kilometres high—the largest of any eruption this century. Within five weeks, winds about 20 kilometres above the surface had spread a veil of volcanic dust around some 50 percent of the planet. Veteran astronauts aboard the space shuttle *Atlantis* that summer reported that they had never seen the earth look so hazy.

The death toll from Mount St. Helens eruption in 1980: 57 people, 5,000 black-tailed deer, 200 black bears, 1,500 elk and countless birds.

Following the eruption, satellite and aircraft observations revealed a 25 to 30 percent decline in the solar radiation reaching the ground. Temperatures began dropping soon after Mount Pinatubo erupted. In 1992, Pinatubo's shadowy plume cut almost half a degree from the average global temperature of about 15°C, nearly counteracting, at least temporarily, 100 years of global greenhouse warming. The cooling might have been even greater had the eruption not coincided with an El Niño—a pronounced warming of the Pacific Ocean water off the coast of South America known to cause a 0.2°C global warming. In Canada the cooling was most pronounced in the east, where average temperatures varied from 1°C to 2°C below normal—the coldest in about 20 years. Many easterners were also quick to blame Pinatubo for the rainiest, gloomiest and coolest summer in a century.

A similar coincidence of a low-latitude volcanic eruption and an El Niño warming occurred in 1982, when El Chichón erupted in Mexico. Rich in sulphur dioxide, El Chichón produced a dust veil 20 times larger than that from Washington State's Mount St. Helens on May 18, 1980, enough to lower the surface temperature in the Northern Hemisphere by a few tenths of a degree. Precisely when and how much cooling took place is impossible to determine, however, because the concurrent El Niño warming was the largest such event this century.

The notion that volcanic eruptions can influence the weather dates back more than 200 years. The ever-curious Benjamin Franklin was among the first to propose the connection. While serving as American ambassador to France in 1785, Franklin speculated that Europe's unusually harsh winter in 1783–84 was due in part to a "permanent dry fog" that had drifted eastward following the 1783 explosion of the Laki volcano in Iceland.

Today it is generally accepted that large volcanic eruptions can affect the weather. The extent of that influence depends on the composition and height of the plume and on the latitude of the volcano.

The eruption of Krakatoa on a small island between Java and Sumatra on August 27, 1883, registered on barometers halfway around the world in London. In fact, it continued to do so up to nine days later, when the echoes of the volcanic report were making their seventh circuit of the earth.

The plume consists of ash and gases, mainly water vapour, carbon dioxide and sulphur dioxide. It is the volume of sulphur dioxide expelled into the stratosphere, not the more spectacular clouds of dust and ash, that most affects global weather. The more emitted, the greater the impact will likely be. Within a few months of an eruption, gravity draws most of the ash particles into the lower atmosphere, where rain and snow remove them within a few days or weeks. The sulphur dioxide in the stratosphere bonds rapidly with water vapour in the presence of sunlight, producing tiny droplets of sulphuric acid that coalesce into a dense haze of aerosols—fine liquid or solid particles. These acidic droplets are so small and light that they remain in the stratosphere for one to three years, deflecting some of the sun's energy and cooling the earth's lower atmosphere and surface. This cooling is partly offset by warming, since the aerosol also absorbs infrared radiation reflected from the earth's surface. In the case of Pinatubo, the overall result was a slight cooling of the lower atmosphere.

The height of the plume helps to determine how widespread and persistent the effects will be. The higher it rises, the longer volcanic gases will stay in the atmosphere and the longer they are likely to affect the weather. For example, the plume from the eruption of Mount St. Helens reached a height of only 24 kilometres—considerably lower than Pinatubo's—and contained little sulphur dioxide. The most notable weather effects were cooler temperatures near the mountain for three or four days immediately following the eruption, as volcanic ash temporarily blocked out the sun. But no long-term or widespread weather effects were recorded.

As for the latitude of the volcano, scientists suspect that large sulphur-rich eruptions near the equator have the greatest impact on weather. Air-circulation patterns there are more likely to carry the volcanic debris into both hemispheres, clouding more of the planet. Plumes from mid-latitude eruptions disperse well east and west, but are much slower to spread north or south. In terms of global effect, Mount St. Helens' eruption was a non-event. Estimated at one-tenth the energy of Krakatoa's, Mount St. Helens was too far

Mary Shelley's *Frankenstein* is instantly recognized as one of the world's great horror stories, but few people know that it owes its origins to the weather. The book was written in the summer of 1816, the famous "year without a summer," when unseasonably cold weather struck parts of North America and Europe. Fourteen months earlier, volcano Tamboro erupted, spreading a veil of dust that altered weather patterns around the world. The rainy, chilly summer on Lake Geneva in Switzerland prevented Mary Shelley and her companions from going outdoors. To pass the time, they began to tell ghost stories. A ghost-story-writing contest developed and Mary wrote *Frankenstein*.

north, erupted sideways (not straight up) and threw too little of the sulphur-rich debris needed to significantly affect the weather. Furthermore, the ejecta's height of only about 24 kilometres was relatively low as such energetic eruptions go.

Cooling aside, there is no proven link between increased volcanic activity and unusual weather. Major volcanic eruptions are often followed by spells of gloomy weather, cool wet summers, prolonged winters, droughts and early frosts. However, the same conditions could also be attributed to weather's random variability.

Rafts of floating pumice, some of them thick enough to support men, crossed the Indian Ocean in 10 months, and were still seen two years after the eruption of Krakatoa.

Looking back at some of the big eruptions in the past two centuries, we can easily see how people started making a connection between volcanoes and bad weather. The April 1815 eruption of Tamboro in Indonesia—considered the most explosive volcanic eruption in the past 5,000 years—emitted about 16 times more ash and gas than Mount Pinatubo and killed 92,000 people. A year later, Tamboro's cloud caused remarkably strange weather across Europe and northeastern North America. With average surface temperatures 1°C to 3°C below normal, heavy snows fell in June and hard frosts occurred in July and August, killing crops and denuding trees. Many birds and newly shorn sheep died from exposure, and crop failures brought ruin, famine and disease. As a result, 1816 became widely known as "the year without a summer."

Similar weather has been associated with other explosive volcanoes. Krakatoa—an island in Indonesia between Java and Sumatra—erupted in May and August

For months after the eruption of Krakatoa, the fine volcanic dust and aerosol caused such brilliant red sunset afterglows that on several occasions fire engines were called out in the northeastern United States to extinguish apparent fires. Vivid sunsets, white suns at noon, rings of pink, red, orange-rose and brown colour continued to be seen for the next three years.

1883, propelling clouds of ash and gas to an altitude of 50 kilometres. The explosions were heard 5,000 kilometres away in Australia, and the sea waves generated by the eruptions were detected in the Atlantic Ocean 17,000 kilometres away. The region was plunged into darkness for almost three days. In addition, Northern Hemisphere temperatures cooled about 0.5°C to 0.8°C, and blazing red sunsets and strange haloes around the sun and moon were created for one or two years following the eruption.

The famous climate researcher H.H. Lamb found that most of the 20th century was markedly quiet in the number of significant volcanic explosions compared with the period from 1500 to 1912. The only notable eruptions since 1912 were Mount Agung in 1963, El Chichón in 1982, and Pinatubo in 1991. During the previous four centuries by contrast, there was, on the average, one eruption every four years.

Since the 1980 eruption of Mount St. Helens, scientists have been using satellites and airplanes to learn more about how volcanoes affect the weather. It now appears that the most likely short-lived regional effect is a modest temperature reduction of typically 0.3°C to 0.5°C in the year following an eruption and a 0.1°C to 0.3°C decline two years after. In theory, this cooling and increased cloud cover could in turn change the normal pattern of weather circulation for several months, including the path of the jet stream and the presence or absence of stationary high-pressure systems that are often associated with weather extremes and spells of unusual weather. During the summer of 1992—a year after Mount Pinatubo erupted—the jet stream wandered farther south than normal, bringing more rain, cooler temperatures and increased cloud cover to central and eastern Canada. The daily weather map in July looked more like one in May.

Atmospheric scientists believe that in addition to cooling the earth, Mount Pinatubo's gases, some 25 million tonnes, may have contributed to the destruction of as much as 15 percent of the earth's imperiled ozone layer in the Northern Hemisphere. With less ozone, more harmful ultraviolet radiation reaches the surface. Fortunately, ozone can slowly rebuild itself. Pinatubo's blast also produced many colourful and enduring sunrises and sunsets, striking solar rings, green suns and blue moons.

Because a single volcanic eruption affects the weather for only a couple of years, some scientists question whether volcanoes can actually change the climate in the long term. For many years, volcanoes were considered a prime cause for initiating glaciers. Some periods of global cooling and increased glaciation have coincided with exceptionally high volcanic activity. For example, the period from 1500 to 1850, known as the Little Ice Age, experienced several major volcanic eruptions and some of the worst summers and coolest winters on record across North America and Europe. However, there is

In addition to cooling the earth, Pinatubo diminished the earth's protective ozone layer as it came into contact with the ash and gas. Some experts estimate that as much as 10 percent of the ozone was destroyed, though ozone does replace itself over time.

little solid evidence to prove a link between volcano activity and ice ages. Indeed, a case can be made for the reverse. The stress of continental glaciers pressing down on the earth's crust may trigger vulcanism.

ARCTIC HAZE

Crystal-clear air, pure and sparkling, used to be an Arctic hallmark. Travellers in the 19th century reported almost unbelievable visibility, spotting mountain peaks 200 kilometres away, poking over the horizon. Today, between February and May, you'd be lucky to see 30 kilometres through the hazy Arctic atmosphere. The Arctic's winter air has become tarnished, dimmed by a dirty blanket of reddish brown smog that clogs the air, acidifies the precipitation and leaves telltale smears on the landscape. Known simply as Arctic haze, it arrives each fall and winter—a totally unexpected phenomenon recorded nowhere else on earth.

People puzzled over the Arctic's hazy air long before they knew its origin. A century ago, Norwegian adventurers trekking across the polar ice pondered mysterious dark stains on the snow surface and in melt pools. As far back as 1914, an Inuit guide referred to the misty haze that shrouded distant summits as *poo-jok*, Inukitut for "fog." An early theory held that the haze was sand blowing in from the Gobi Desert. A few scientists argued that it was just ice crystals and blowing snow. Pilots like RCAF Wing Commander Keith Greenaway flying weather reconnaissance over the Canadian northwest in the late 1940s were surprised by the thickness of this "ice crystal haze." Others suggested northern sources such as smoke from the naturally burning Smoking Hills near the Mackenzie River delta or exhaust from machines involved in oil exploration on the Beaufort Sea shelf. What they had to rule out, though, were nearby towns, mines and oil and gas refineries. The Arctic just doesn't have major pollution sources.

Environment Canada estimated that Arctic air pollution increased by 75 percent between 1956 and 1986, paralleling a doubling of acidic sulphur-dioxide emissions in Europe and the territory formerly known as the Soviet Union.

So entrenched was the myth of the pristine North that scientists refused to believe the Arctic could be widely polluted. "It was not until the 1970s that a series of air-chemistry measurements conducted first at Barrow, Alaska, and then at Mould Bay, N.W.T., showed that Arctic haze is not natural but more human in origin," says Len Barrie, an Environment Canada scientist and a kind of modern-day explorer of the Arctic atmosphere.

The haze, in fact, is an airborne swamp of industrial pollutants, mostly sulphur and nitrogen compounds found as a gas, together with aerosols. Over time these transform into microparticles of sulphuric and nitric acids, similar to the acid-rain pollution that plagues Europe and North America.

Theoretically, when the air is clean, one can see as far as 220 kilometres. However, haze in the Arctic can limit visibility to a mere 30 kilometres or less.

Using aircraft equipped with lasers and high-volume vacuum samplers, Canadian scientists have flown back and forth through the haze layers in order to measure its extent and concentration. The haze is Arctic-wide, blanketing virtually the entire region north of 60°N. It makes the

Research lab at Alert, NWT, shrouded in Arctic haze. *Carbon Cycle Research Lab/Environment Canada.*

Arctic winter air 10 to 20 times more polluted than Antarctica's and some 10 times more polluted than that over the least polluted non-industrial regions elsewhere in North America.

Where does the stuff come from? How does it reach the Arctic? Why does it peak in the winter and spring and vanish in summer? Over the past 20 years, a small, highly motivated group of research scientists—glaciologists, meteorologists and atmospheric chemists—from Canada, the United States and Norway have tried to answer these questions.

To find the source of the polluted air, they first hunted for its path by looking at routinely observed winds and pressure fields. But that approach was frustrated by the scarcity of meteorological data from the Arctic, and the enormous distances, some 8,000 to 10,000 kilometres, back to sources in mid-latitude.

The answer lay in finding the villain's chemical "fingerprints." In 1980, Len Barrie and Kenneth Rahn, a research professor at the University of Rhode Island, developed a tracing method that identified a distinctive chemical signature in an air mass, which they could trace back to its region, if not very factory, of origin. They were able to determine the type of raw fuel and ore used in refineries by comparing the isotopes in a polluted air sample found in the Arctic with that of the raw

So far, at least, the air at the South Pole remains pure—perhaps the cleanest air on earth and about a tenth of that found in the Arctic. The Southern Hemisphere contains relatively few sources of industrial pollution, and its wind patterns do not sweep pollutants towards the pole.

material (ores and fuel). The composition of lead in emissions from refineries in Russia, Western Europe and North America varies, they found, depending upon the region.

Using this model, Barrie and his colleagues discovered that up to two-thirds of the Arctic's haze originates in the heavily industrialized nations of Eastern Europe and Russia, and the remainder in Western Europe. North America contributes less than 4 percent. This is no reason for us to feel smug: it just happens that the prevailing winds carry our pollution east over the Atlantic Ocean, where storms clean the air. However, European and Russian air masses are propelled northwest into the Arctic in winter.

Canada's first air pollution monitoring laboratory at Alert, N.W.T., in the High Arctic, is the most northerly permanent environmental research laboratory in the world. It was opened in August 1986. The purpose of the laboratory is to measure the concentration of industrial pollutants—for example, carbon dioxide, halogenated organic compounds and sulphates—and to monitor the changes in their concentrations over time.

In the fall and winter, the Arctic atmosphere loads up with airborne contaminants. The grimy winter air is routinely 20 to 40 times dirtier than in summer for at least three reasons related to meteorology. The great dome of colder, heavier surface air that traps pollution over the Arctic is largely a winter phenomenon. In the inversion, increased stability and stagnation form an invisible barrier 400 to 800 metres above ground. This prevents incoming contaminants from mixing vertically, and traps what little pollution is released locally from Arctic towns and power plants.

Second, the large weather systems that control the movement of pollutants into, through and out of the Arctic are particularly vigorous in winter, strengthened by marked north-south temperature contrasts. In addition, a zone of strong northward flow is created by intense storms linked with huge continental high-pressure areas. In summer, by contrast, the weather circulation is much weaker, and air generally moves from north to south.

Finally, during the fall and winter seasons, haze particles have a longer residence time in the atmosphere than in the summer. Because the air passes over what is essentially a frozen desert, there is little rain or snow to wash out pollutants. In the summer, more abundant rains and low-lying clouds associated with drizzle and fog scrub out the pollution.

How long has haze been polluting the Arctic? The answer was found in the ice of Ellesmere Island by Dr. Roy Koerner, a glaciologist with the Geological Survey of Canada. In the 1980s, he pulled up drill cores from centuries of accumulated snow and ice, analyzed their acidity levels and found a century-long record of industrial pollution. Levels of acidity in the century's first half were constant but changed dramatically after 1956, increasing by some 75 percent over the next two and a half decades. This increase mirrored the doubling of acidic sulphur-dioxide emissions worldwide and included a new mess of airborne toxic contaminants, including herbicides and pesticides such as lindane and DDT; heavy metals such as lead, mercury and vanadium; and industrial organic compounds like solvents, dioxin and PCBs.

According to French scientists, snow that fell on Greenland in 1967 contained seven times more lead than snow that fell in 1989. Concentrations of two other heavy metal pollutants, cadmium and zinc, more than halved in the same period. The decline mirrors a drop in heavy-metal pollution in the lower atmosphere in the past two decades, and a switch to unleaded gasoline.

Whereas we now know a fair amount about the composition, variation and origin of haze, we know a lot less about its effects on the precarious Arctic ecosystem and the global environment. Most obvious is the sharp reduction of visibility. But more significantly, haze alters the balance between heat and cold—and possibly, the climate. The black, sooty aerosols in the air absorb the sun's heat,

---

Although Arctic winter-spring pollution levels are not as bad as that in southern Canadian cities, they are roughly one-fifth the average levels around Lake Erie between Detroit, Cleveland, Buffalo and Toronto. The Arctic concentrations are about 10 times higher than background levels in other remote areas of the Northern Hemisphere.

warming the lower atmosphere. Soot on snow and ice also absorbs heat from the sun's rays that would otherwise be largely reflected back into the sky. As the snow and ice cover melts, less heat is reflected, which accelerates the overall warming and melts more snow and ice, and so the cycle continues.

Recently, however, some good news has come from Alert, N.W.T., where Environment Canada's research laboratory has monitored the northern atmosphere since 1979. (The Alert observatory is the most northerly permanent environmental research facility in the world.) The trend in Arctic haze, which began accelerating in the 1950s, has been stopped. And more good news: although the sulphate content has remained roughly the same, concentrations of some toxic organic contaminants and heavy metals have fallen dramatically. Levels of the insecticide lindane at Alert have dropped 90 percent since 1979, and lead concentrations have shrunk by 55 percent since 1980. This decline is partly due to international efforts to eliminate lead in gasoline and to control toxic releases.

Measures aimed at curbing pollutants that compose haze are working. Still, much work remains to be done in curtailing pollution and identifying polluting sources and pathways before the Arctic air is returned to its once-pristine condition.

HALOS, SUNDOGS AND SUN PILLARS

One day in the summer of 1865, tragedy befell a party of British and French mountain climbers in the Alps: after making the first ascent of the Matterhorn, four men tumbled from the steep slopes and were killed. Shortly afterwards, a surviving member of the team, Edward Whymper, saw a startling and poignant phenomenon in the sky: a large circle of light with three ghostly crosses, "a strange and awesome sight … at such a moment," as Whymper wrote. The alpinist was not gazing at a spectral vision but at an unusual combination of figures created by distorted sunlight—a halo, circle and pillar. Its timing was astonishing but purely coincidental, and is perhaps the most famous example of such solar displays.

◄ **The sky is often blue on earth, but skies are not blue on every planet. The sky on Mars is pink; it's black on the moon, and yellow on Venus.**

Almost everyone is familiar with lightning, rainbows and the northern lights, but few people are aware of the dazzling variety of bright, sometimes coloured, spots, patches, rings and arcs occasionally on display in the sky. Although halos, sundogs and sun pillars occur quite often, these optics are rarely seen by the casual observer. Few people know where and when to look for them. This is a pity because not only are these phenomena beautiful, but they can also tell us something about the clouds overhead and help us predict changes in the weather.

◄ **In A.D. 40, the Roman College of Soothsayers foretold good fortune from an observation of three suns that appeared in the sky—i.e., sundogs or parhelia. However, the soothsayers missed the mark, as the following year was not a good one for Rome.**

Optical phenomena are the result of light refracting (bending) through or reflecting (bouncing) off tiny, floating ice crystals in the air or high clouds. They come in a great assortment of patterns, which are determined by three factors: the shape of the crystals themselves, the path light takes through them, and the alignment of the crystals as they fall or are suspended in the air. First, although all ice crystals are six sided, like snowflakes, they have several different shapes. The most common are six-sided plates and columns, but bullet-shaped crystals, some with flat caps, also occur.

Second, since ice crystals are not round like raindrops, light can travel in many pathways

Although sky effects are caused mostly by ice crystals, they can occur throughout the year, even on the warmest summer day, because the upper extent of the atmosphere is always extremely cold.

through them, entering an end or side and exiting from a different facet; or light can reflect off the crystal surfaces. The different paths create different light patterns.

Third, the ways in which ice crystals twist and turn when falling through the air increase the variety of effects they create. Some crystals are randomly aligned in the air, while others are ordered identically, like soldiers on parade facing the same direction. Each orientation can produce its own distinct optical effect. When ice crystals are very small, constant bombardment by moving air molecules keeps them suspended randomly (at all angles to the ground). But large crystals may fall facedownward, much like a dinner plate on being dropped. Each orientation produces its own distinct optical effect.

The most spectacular and commonly observed figure is the halo—a circle of light around the sun or moon. Most halos are created by light entering one of the side faces of each ice crystal and exiting through a different side face after changing direction (refracting) about 22°. The crystals must be of uniform size and point in all directions to produce the circular diffusion. Larger, fainter halos sometimes occur farther from the sun or moon, and are called "great," or 46°, halos. They are formed either when light enters the top of each crystal, refracts and emerges from one of the sides, or when light enters one side and passes out the bottom.

A halo may appear as a complete ring when the sky is covered with a uniform sheet of wispy, high cirrostratus cloud. More often, however, the cloud covers only part of the sky, and as a result, only segments of a halo are visible. Usually the ring of light appears whitish, but on occasion the colours of the rainbow may be seen faintly, with red on the inside, yellow and green in the middle and bluish white on the outside.

Solar halos are more common than lunar halos, which are seldom noticed unless the moon is full. (Because the extremely bright light of the sun can damage your eyes when looking into it, always block it out with an open hand or a book held at arm's length.) Halos occur most frequently when the sun is near the horizon and blurred by a thin veil of cirrus clouds. They can occur at any time of year, but the spring is often the best viewing season. Halos are frequent Prairie phenomena because of the region's typically sunny weather and low temperatures and the prevalence of high, thin cirroform clouds.

You may have observed bright, sometimes rainbow-coloured, blazes on either or both sides of the sun. These are commonly called sundogs (presumably because they "dog" or mock the sun), but the technical name for them is parhelia. They occasionally occur, less brightly, around the moon, and are called moondogs or paraselenae.

Sundogs are created when sunlight hits plate-shaped ice crystals falling in a uniform alignment with their six sides vertical. Such crystals, at least the larger ones, tend to float like parachutes with their top and bottom faces oriented horizontally. Sunlight enters one of the vertical side faces, refracts once, traverses the interior of the crystal and refracts again as it exits. This bends the light about 22°, creating mirror solar images about 22° from the sun—slightly outside the 22° halo that often occurs at the same time. Although most people have never seen them, sundogs are visible about 10 times a year in most parts of Canada. The most brilliant ones appear when the cold air is dense with plate crystals, when the crystals fall without excessive flutter or tumbling and when the sun is low in the sky. Look for a cold sunny morning or evening, when the sun is near the horizon.

On a few clear days, you may glimpse a lone streak of emerald green light shooting straight up from the sun at the horizon. Called a green flash, it only lasts a second. The green flash can occur at sunrise or sunset, when the clear atmosphere disperses that very first or final ray of the sun's white light into the colours of the spectrum. The rays of the shorter blue end of the spectrum are scattered and lost, so the next hue, green, flashes before your eyes.

The simplest interaction of sunlight or moonlight with ice crystals occurs when light reflects off the crystals to produce pillars. They are vertical streaks of light stretching to a height of 5 to 10 degrees above, and occasionally below, the sun. Most com-

························➤

The best "viewing" weather for spotting halos, sundogs and sun pillars includes:

- **cold Arctic air mass air temperature near the surface of about -17˚C**
- **bright sunshine—i.e., after the passage of an intense cold front**
- **blowing snow or a trace of cumulus fractus clouds**
- **moderate to strong winds**

mon at sunset or sunrise, these glittering columns are created when a beam of sunlight reflects off the flat bottoms of descending plate crystals in cirrus cloud or extremely cold air. Because they are caused by reflection, sun pillars are the same colour as the sun. If the sun is very low, the pillar may reflect the red hues of sunset (or sunrise). Pillars are sometimes confused with crepuscular (twilight) rays, which are rays of sunlight—often spectacular—that pierce gaps in a layer of low cloud, or radiate upward through gaps in the lumpy tops of cumuliform clouds just above or below the horizon.

Sundogs and all related halo phenomena were regarded with awe by early peoples and were thought to forewarn of troubled times. They were also seen as harbingers of foul weather. This is apparent in the following folk sayings:

- Ring around the moon, rain is coming soon.
- When the sun is in his house, it will rain soon.
- The bigger and brighter the ring, the nearer the wet.
- The moon with a circle brings water in her beak.
- A bright circle round the sun denotes a storm and cooler weather.
- The circle of the moon never filled a pond; the circle of the sun wets a shepherd.

In fact, a halo around the sun or moon *is* one of the better weather predictors visible in the sky. The high cirrus stratus clouds, the so-called mare's tails, that cause halos are often the first visible sign of an approaching warm front, bringing wet weather. Canadian studies have shown that on two out of three occasions, rain or snow will arrive within 18 to 36 hours after a halo has been spotted.

The chances of accurately predicting rain or snow from halos depends upon how close you are to one of the corridors taken most commonly by storms. A halo in Thunder Bay may mean there is a 30 percent chance of rain the next day, whereas rings over Montreal might indicate a 65 percent chance of rain in 24 hours. Montreal is in a storm track, and Thunder Bay is not. If, in addition to seeing a halo, you observe falling barometric pressure, an increasing southerly wind and progressive thickening of cloud from the west, you can be more confident that rain or snow is on the way.

There are many other less commonly known optical effects produced by ice crystals—double halos, the Parry arc and subsuns, to name a few. Most are not as rare as you might expect. What is rare, however, and sure to stir the imagination, is seeing two or more optical effects together, as Edward Whymper did on that fateful day in the Alps in 1865. The skies are constantly changing, so look up and treat yourself to the many spectacles that have struck awe in skywatchers throughout history.

A weather observer near Bristol, England, diligently watched for halos in the sky during a 12-year period. He found that of the 80 haloes sighted, 71 were around the sun and nine around the moon; 39 haloes lasted less than five minutes, 11 more than an hour. As for the adage that halos are a sure sign of rain or snow, he found that on only 45 occasions out of 80 did rain follow within 48 hours.

Snowflakes, Snowballs and Snowrollers

Is it ever too cold to snow?

You may think so! On the coldest days of the year, the sky is often sunny and cloudless and there is "no snow" in the air.

You may have noticed that the heaviest snowfalls with the largest and stickiest snowflakes typically occur when the temperature is near freezing rather than very low. For some Prairie cities, March is, on average, both the mildest and snowiest of the winter months. This is because warm air holds more moisture than cold air, which means that more water can fall as snow. For instance, at −30°C, saturated air contains only one-tenth of the water vapour it would contain at −5°C. In addition, at very low temperatures, ice crystals are dry and do not bond well. Instead, they settle out as tiny single crystals rather than aggregate as snowflakes.

On the other hand, even in the coldest regions of Canada—where there is very little water vapour in the air—very fine snow still falls. At Eureka, N.W.T.—arguably the coldest place in Canada—15.2 centimetres of snow fell on December 23, 1983, in spite of a temperature of −21.3°C. In fact, in December, January and February, an average of 10 centimetres of snow falls at Eureka. But to reach that meagre total, snow occurs an astonishing 82 of 90 days: that's 13 days with a measurable amount (above 0.2 centimetres) and 69 with only a trace amount.

The biggest snowflake recorded in Canada fell in Halifax on February 22, 1986. The six-sided crystal measured five centimetres in diameter. But it was dwarfed by snow flakes the size of small pizzas that fell near Fort Keogh, Montana, on January 28, 1887.

So while the notion that it can be too cold to snow is erroneous, the amount of snowfall is usually less the colder it gets.

What are snowrollers?

Snowrollers are giant natural snowballs. Mother Nature gave Regina thousands of them just before Christmas in 1993. Snowrollers have a certain mystery to them, like other weather oddities such as ball lightning, white tornadoes and waterspouts. Although they occur in Canada each year, they are rare and form mostly at night or in the early morning. Moreover, they are the stuff of kids' pranks: a field of huge snowballs without telling footprints or a single eyewitness.

A really good snowroller is cylindrical with hollowed-out ends, often with a hole extending through it lengthwise. As a result, snowrollers have been compared to ladies' muffs, rolls of light cotton batting or a rolled-up carpet. They range in size from eggs to small barrels, but are typically the size of a football. Tracks behind them mark the path along which the wind has been blowing and are typically less than one centimetre deep and several metres long, though they may extend the length of a football field. Snowrollers may weigh up to four to six kilograms, but, unlike handmade snowballs, they are composed of such loose and fluffy material that they fall to pieces at the slightest handling.

Snowrollers are rare because conditions for their formation must be perfect. They need:

Snowrollers have been observed in many parts of the world. On March 4, 1980, snowrollers formed on the island of Cyprus. The snow happened to be of the required consistency for snowrollers to form and roll to the bottom of the hill. All were subsequently found to have pebbles at their centres.

- a layer of newly fallen, light, feathery snowflakes, followed by
- a warming, say 1 or 2 degrees above freezing, sufficient to melt but not thaw the layers of snow, so that the soft and damp snow crystals cling to one another (which leads to rolling rather than drifting), and
- strong, gusty winds of at least 45 km/h to pick up the snow and start it somersaulting along.

It also helps to have a gently sloping smooth surface, where the force of gravity helps the wind roll the snow along. The best surface is a

> **Before the auto-mobile age, the term snowroller was applied to horse-drawn vehicles consisting of two large wooden rollers that flattened snow on public roads to make a smooth path for sleighs.**

smooth crust of old snow with no tufts of grass or other projections to impede the roller.

Sticky snow, warm air and strong winds provide perfect snowroller conditions. However, something has to be missing: if not, snowrollers would be as common as rainbows and sundogs. The key: What starts the snowball rolling?

Some have suggested it is a strong downward gust that scoops up fragments of snow or ice off the surface and sets the roll in motion, much like a breeze lifts the edge of a paper lying on the ground. Others suggest that flakes hit the snow surface at a sharp angle, tip over and, are immediately caught by a wind gust and pushed along.

Once in motion, rollers tumble onward until the wind slackens or until they grow so large that they become lopsided and fall over, or until the ground levels off too much for the wind to propel the mass of snow farther.

Snowrollers develop somewhere in Canada each winter. They are most common in southern Alberta, where winds tend to be strong and

A cylindrical snowball that formed during the night south of Porcupine Plain, Saskatchewan, in February 1997. *Environment Canada.*

temperatures rise rapidly. But chances are you will see snowrollers on a steep roof before you spot them in an open field.

Are any two snowflakes alike?

It has long been said that like human fingerprints, no two snowflakes are exactly alike. Is this true? Well, it depends on how you define "alike." If alike means that snowflakes have to *look* the same, then the cherished belief isn't true. After all, to most observers, a snowflake is a snowflake. And there are lots of them. Over the past five billion years—the lifetime of the earth—an estimated one undecillion flakes (one followed by 35 zeros) have blanketed the earth. Since all snowflakes start the same way and are usually composed of six-sided or six-pointed crystals of ice, it would seem reasonable that a duplicate would one day appear, if only someone would take the time to look.

Weight of one cubic metre of old, accumulated snow in Winnipeg: 190 kilos; in Quebec City : 220 kilos; Whistler, B.C.: 430 kilos.

Wilson Bentley, or "Snowflake" as he was better known, of Jericho, Vermont, spent his lifetime looking for twin flakes. The farmer and amateur meteorologist put nearly 6,000 flakes under the microscope, photographing and recording each delicate feature. Eventually, he identified 100 different crystal structures, but identical snowflakes eluded him. He died in 1931, his search unresolved.

Others followed in his footsteps. In 1986, two researchers at the United States National Center for Atmospheric Research in Boulder, Colorado, gained some notoriety with their claim of a matching set of snow crystals collected, by means of fixed probes extending from the front of an aircraft, 7,000 metres above Wisconsin. The tiny, column-like crystals with vase-shaped hollow centres were very much alike. After a closer look, however, minute variations in structure and form were discovered.

So why the difficulty tracking down twin flakes? The answer is that probably none exist. So many variables are at play when a snowflake develops, meteorologists say, that the odds of two following identical paths are ridiculously small.

> **Every centimetre of snow that falls on Montreal costs the city's works department $300,000. After every major snowstorm, 3,000 people are dispatched to clear 2,000 kilometres of streets, 3,000 kilometres of sidewalks, 32,000 pedestrian crossings, 7,600 bus stops and 60 subway entrances. Montreal ploughs more snow each winter than any other city in the world, over 42 million tonnes.**

Cumulus clouds stacked high on the horizon forewarn of a winter's storm. Along the cloud's underbelly, water droplets collect; in its upper reaches, where temperatures are well below freezing, ice crystals form. Every snowflake begins as a single ice crystal with most forming around a solid particle known as a freezing nucleus—a floating piece of clay, fine dust, tiny pollen, sea salt, volcanic ash or even a fleck of pollution from a car's exhaust. Water vapour in the surrounding air uses the nucleus as a platform. In a process known as sublimation, the vapour condenses into ice on the surface of this host nucleus without first going through the liquid phase. If the ice crystal continues to grow by sublimation, an individual, intricate and visible snow crystal soon develops. Other ice crystals form without a freezing nucleus. In this case, tiny beads of supercooled water freeze directly into ice at very low temperatures. (Left alone, supercooled water droplets stay unfrozen at temperatures as low as −40°C before hardening spontaneously into ice.)

But in either situation, neither the supercooled liquid droplets nor the individual ice crystals are large enough to fall from clouds as precipitation. To become snowflakes, the ice crystals must grow many times larger; they do so mainly by sublimation of water vapour.

An ice crystal grows by attracting and absorbing water vapour molecules that build on one another in a symmetrical way, thus continually adding to its weight and size. But since each of the thousands of billions of water molecules has an astronomically large number of choices of where to attach itself to the crystal, it is very unlikely that every molecule would line up in exactly the same position as every molecule in another crystal.

Still, the ultimate shape and size of the snow crystal, hence the snowflake, depend on temperature and, to some extent, on the amount of water vapour available in the cloud. Even slight changes in the cloud environment can have a marked effect on the crystal structure:

- Crystals that grow in air at −20°C or colder, and with little available moisture, form hollow prisms or hexagonal columns similar in shape to a length of pencil
- Between −23°C to −18°C, crystals are compacted into flat wafers called hexagonal plates
- With more moisture available between −17°C and −12°C, larger crystals grow into delicate, six-pointed stars called dendrites, their shape reminiscent of human nerve cells by the same name
- In warmer air but still below freezing, crystals grow into splinter-shaped bits of ice known as needles; and at freezing, crystals take on the shape of thin hexagons

Thirty-six percent of Canada's precipitation occurs as snow, compared with 5 percent for the world.

Only when the ice crystal has attracted sufficient mass does it begin its journey earthward. At some point, the ice crystal will become heavy enough to fall at about 50 centimetres per second. During its descent, the falling ice crystal collides and coalesces with supercooled droplets and other ice crystals. As this multi-crystal aggregate becomes larger, it falls faster. Eventually, it drops out of the cloud as a snowflake.

Nearly anything can happen to snowflakes as they drift and tumble earthward. Pieces break off, evaporate or melt. Flakes bump into one another and sometimes bind together. Others pick up frozen water droplets and tiny particles—all processes that change a snowflake's shape, design and water content. When falling snowflakes begin to melt, they stick to just about anything, even to each other. In some cases, hundreds and thousands of ice crystals may cling together to form gigantic snowflakes. Also, the greater the distance snowflakes fall, the larger they become. In general, snowflakes are less than half a centimetre in diameter. But on rare occasions, they can

Fresh snow falls each year on roughly a quarter of the earth's land surface, as well as about 10 percent of the oceans. Only one-third of the people in the world have ever kicked the white stuff.

On November 21, 1997, the owner of Ski Martock, a ski hill at Falmouth, Nova Scotia, was commissioned to send 50 tonnes of fresh Canadian snow to the sunny climes of Puerto Rico. The snow made the 3,000 kilometre trip in a refrigerated container, arriving in time for a four-day celebration to kick off the Christmas season.

coalesce into gigantic snowflakes. Back on January 28, 1887, at Fort Keogh, Montana, monster snowflakes "larger than milk pans" and measuring 38 centimetres in diameter were reported.

For two crystals to look the same under a microscope, they would have to attract the same number of molecules of water vapour, the molecules would have to arrange themselves in the same way and each crystal would have had to collide with the same number of other crystals during its long fall to the ground. Even the slightest change in a host of factors, from a rise in air temperature to a whiff of wind, will make two flakes different. So are there any two snowflakes that are exactly alike? Very unlikely indeed!

FROZEN FROSTY FLAKES

One cold morning a farmer went to his back door to holler for his pigs. It was so cold out that as he yelled, his words froze in the air. His pigs didn't come until his words thawed out in the spring.

—Tall Weather Tale

The curious thing about this exaggeration is that it carries a certain truth.

When each breath you exhale leaves a trail of frozen mist, you don't have to look at the thermometer to know it's uncomfortably cold outside. At −40°C, warm breath condenses instantly into ice crystals, forming what meteorologists call ice fog—one weather phenomenon largely caused by human activities. So in a way, spoken words do solidify into floating frozen flakes.

Ice fog is fairly common in interior Alaska, Siberia and northern

Canada. Prairie cities can expect an average of 75 to 100 hours of it each winter. The exception is Winnipeg, which has averaged only 35 hours of it a year since 1953, probably because there are fewer sources of water vapour there. By comparison, even though it is surrounded by water, Montreal averages only 5 hours of ice fog annually since it has fewer days of extremely cold temperatures. Sometimes the frozen fog hangs around for several days before disappearing. In what was surely Canada's most extended spell of meteorological claustrophobia, much of Edmonton was enveloped in an eerie thickness for 23 days in January 1969. During this fog, easily remembered by local weather watchers with fondness and much pride, the *Edmonton Journal* received many requests for its certificates declaring that the bearer had just survived nearly four weeks of bitterly cold temperatures. Unknown to most, the citizens themselves were responsible for the cold fog.

Herds of caribou generate banks of ice fog during very low temperatures. The breath of a trotting animal discharges into the air about six grams of water vapour a minute.

Ice and water fog look much the same: a dull, grey shroud that reduces visibility, playing havoc with airline schedules, driving conditions and outdoor activities. But ice fog is generally shallower—typically ranging from 10 to 50 metres in depth, and occasionally up to 100 metres. Nonetheless, ice fog is more persistent than water fog. Since ice particles are only one-tenth the size of water droplets, they are lighter and slower to settle out. The fog can linger for days.

Air in Toronto at 20°C can hold 255 times more water in the vapour state than air at -45°C in Whitehorse.

Thick ice fog may reduce street-level visibility to arm's length. Inside the frozen fog layer, the sun appears as a dimly lit orb, and streetlights take on a ghostly glow. But from outside the fog layer, vertical visibility is surprisingly good. Pilots circling an airport can nearly always see the runway through a layer of ice fog. However, on the final stages of an aircraft's landing, the runway disappears because the horizontal fog layer extends for several kilometres.

In the Arctic and sub-Arctic regions, ice fog is often a greater health hazard than extremely frigid temperatures. Many pedestrian/automobile accidents are a direct result of heavy ice fog and its restrictions on visibility. Northern people, after several days of ice fog have deprived them of precious sunshine, may become miserable and stressed, causing absenteeism from work or school and lower productivity. Moreover, ice fog can be a form of air pollution. There have even been incidents of people suffocating after inhaling an excess number of ice crystals that had accumulated around their noses. More often, ice-fog crystals have caused respiratory problems when inhaled.

One of the more life-threatening risks of being out of doors in an ice fog is that ice crystals may accumulate around one's nose when inhaling and cause suffocation.

How does ice fog form? In a manner similar to that of condensation trails left behind in the exhaust of high-flying jet aircraft. When warm moist gases, usually invisible, are discharged into the cold air, excess water condenses rapidly into either liquid drops or ice crystals, depending upon the temperature and upon the presence of condensation nuclei. When the tempetrature plunges, it takes very little moisture to produce dense ice fog because colder air holds less water. For example, saturated air at 20°C can hold about 20 grams of water vapour per cubic metre, but at –40°C, it can hold only one-tenth of a gram—200 times less.

The majority of ice fog events last for under 7 hours. One of Canada's longest ice fog episodes, 171 hours, occurred at Pelly Bay on the Arctic coast. At Resolute Airport, over one 20-year period, there were 41 episodes of ice fog lasting longer than 24 hours.

Contrary to what we would think, ice fog does not result from a moist air mass; rather, it comes from the heated water vapour over local sources. Evaporation from sewage lagoons and from dumping cooling water at power plants contributes large quantities of water vapour. Exhaust gases from incinerators, and automobile engines also contribute. A gasoline engine generates one litre of water for every litre of fuel used by the engine.

In addition, natural sources of vapour are important local sources for ice fog.

These include fast-flowing streams and open ocean waters, as well as exhalations from animals. At –40°C, moist breath precipitates into ice crystals. In his book, *My Life with the Eskimo*, the renowned Arctic explorer Vilhjalmur Stefansson wrote of seeing clouds of steam from caribou: "... the air was so calm that where an animal ran past rapidly he left behind him a cloud of steam hovering over his trail and marking it out plainly for a mile behind him."

In clean air, ice fog may not form until temperatures fall to –40°C; however, if the air is dirty, droplets can freeze into ice crystals at the relatively high temperature of –30°C. In northern regions, the air always contains condensation nuclei: soil particles, sea salt, dust, aircraft and vehicle exhausts and other by-products of combustion—even particles of cosmic origin—make it easier for ice crystals to bind together by giving them a platform to build on.

This explains why ice fog has become more prevalent since the turn of the century. Scientists at the Geophysical Institute of the University of Alaska have discovered that in the early 1900s— when fewer people lived in cities and there were fewer cars, airplanes and industries to pollute the air—ice fog rarely occurred in Anchorage at temperatures above –50°C. In the early 1950s, the temperature threshold for ice fog was only –35°C, and more recently it has been near –30°C. It is now easier to freeze words!

In most stations in northern Canada, ice fog occurrence begins between 6 and 8 a.m., reaching a maximum between late morning and mid-afternoon, when people are busiest, and this includes airport operations.

IT'S NOT THE HEAT, IT'S THE HUMIDITY

Say the word *humidity* and most people think of steamy summer days, long sleepless nights and perspiring bodies—almost enough to make you long for frosty January nights. These are reactions to the presence of water vapour, that invisible moisture suspended in the earth's atmosphere. We tend to become aware of water vapour when humidity is high because the air seems sticky, clothes feel damp and our skin is moist, or when it's low because our lips chap and flyaway hair won't behave. More than most elements in the weather, humidity affects our comfort whether we are indoors or out—nearly always increasing our discomfort as it moves above or below average levels.

Water moves between the atmosphere and the surface very quickly. On average, a water molecule that enters the air will remain there for about 10 days. By the end of that time, it will have returned to the surface as rain or snow.

The effect of humidity on humans is almost all bad. High humidity may help to cause migraines, ulcers, clotting and rheumatoid arthritis, not to mention cramps, irritability, exhaustion and muddled thinking. Sticky weather affects a person's appearance too: the complexion is flushed, the skin becomes oily, hair is limp, and to make matters worse, humidity usually makes us look and feel bloated.

Excessive humidity can be downright destructive, corroding metals and causing many materials to decompose. Bacteria sprout in high temperatures with high humidities, causing mildew and mould to develop. Potatoes develop blight and wheat rusts, while paper, leather and manufactured wood products warp and swell. As workers' attention spans shorten, on-the-job accidents and errors increase dramatically. Got a squeaky chair, a guitar that won't stay in tune or a drawer that sticks? It's not the heat, it's the humidity!

High humidity also influences respiration and perspiration in animals. Customs agents in Saudi Arabia found that when the weather gets too damp, narcotic-detector dogs become less effective. In heat and high humidity, farmers claim hogs grow restless, lose their appetites and gain less, and cows milk poorly and conceive fewer offspring.

Humidity is closely linked to human discomfort because of its effect on perspiration. In hot weather, the body regulates its core temperature by sweating. Sweating itself doesn't cool, because the temperature of perspiration is the same as that of the body. As the sweat evaporates, however, it carries heat from the body, cooling the skin. This evaporative process works best when the air is dry. As humidity rises, the moisture-laden atmosphere cannot take as much water away from the skin and absorbs it too slowly to cool efficiently. In extreme conditions, when the body loses large amounts of fluid through perspiration, heat exhaustion and heat stroke may occur. Symptoms include profuse sweating, weakness, nausea, muscle cramps, headache, faintness and feverishness.

Kelowna, B.C., is considered a summer-resort town and Windsor, Ontario, is the thunderstorm capital of Canada, with a less than comfortable summer climate. Yet the average mid-afternoon July temperature at the two places is the same. The difference lies in the relative humidity, which in Kelowna averages 38 percent in July, while in Windsor it is closer to 60 percent.

Although invisible, water vapour is always present in the atmosphere, varying in concentration from almost zero to a maximum of about 4 percent by volume. Water vapour is a vital element in meteorology. It is the only gas that can change into a liquid or solid under ordinary atmospheric conditions, and it is this changeability that results in many features of the weather—clouds, dew, rain, snow, fog and frost.

Warm air can hold more water vapour than cold air. If a specific volume of air at 0°C can hold a quarter litre of water, it can hold a half a litre at 10°C and two litres at 33°C. Air is said to be "saturated" when it is holding all the water vapour it can contain for the prevailing temperature and pressure.

Meteorologists have coined several expressions to describe the air's moisture content. The most familiar, and perhaps the most misunder-

Here's one way to cool off. *Toronto Sun*

stood term, is *relative humidity*. It means the percentage of water vapour that air actually holds compared with what it could hold at a specific temperatureand pressure. It is frequently misunderstood to mean the air's moisture content, or absolute humidity. Relative humidity varies from 100 percent in clouds and fog to 10 percent or less over deserts during the day. Air at 22°C can hold approximately eight grams of water vapour per cubic metre at its capacity. If, however, it contains only four grams then it is only half saturated, and its relative humidity is 50 percent.

By itself, relative humidity tells nothing about how much water is in the air. A high relative humidity does not necessarily mean high humidity. Relative humidity follows air temperature in an inverse way—a decrease in temperature results in an increase in relative humidity, and an increase in temperature causes a decrease in relative humidity. For example, a relative humidity of 70 percent feels more humid when the temperature is 10°C than when the temperature is 20°C. On average, the relative humidity is greatest at dawn, the coolest part of the day, and lowest in mid-afternoon, when the temperature reaches its maximum. It tends to be highest in winter and lowest in summer.

A much better term to describe atmospheric moisture is *dew point*. That is the temperature at which an air mass becomes saturated, usually by cooling. While the air temperature remains above the dew point, the air is unsaturated, that is to say, it is capable of holding additional water vapour. If the air temperature near the ground is 23°C and the dew-point temperature is 13°C, the air must cool 10 degrees to reach saturation. Once it reaches the saturation (its dew point temperature) it releases its excess moisture by forming clouds, rain or fog, or by condensing as dew or frost on cold surfaces, such as grass or vehicles. The dew point does not change with the air temperature. Over the course of a summer day, while relative humidity is rising and falling, the dew point will remain fairly constant as long as the moisture content remains unchanged.

The higher the dew-point temperature, the more moisture in the air. With a dew point of 20°C, most people *feel* uncomfortably sticky, even though the relative humidity may only be 50 percent and the air temperature 32°C.

Over the years, climatologists have proposed several terms for the various combinations of temperature and humidity that are used to describe what hot, humid weather feels like to the average person. These include humiture, apparent temperature, humisery, summer simmer index, heat stress and humidex. Only humidex has gained wide acceptance, and is the one most familiar to Canadians.

Humidex was introduced in Canada on June 24, 1965. It equates the comfort of a humid air mass to that of a hotter air mass with negligible humidity. An air temperature of 32°C with a relative humidity of 75 percent makes it feel like 46°C—i.e., its humidex reading—and the temperature at

A few centuries ago, Roger Bacon discovered that a pound of wool hung suspended for a single night over, but not touching, the surface of water in a well will have absorbed so much of the dampness by morning that its weight increases by slightly more than a pound. A rope knot tied in dry weather will become harder to untie in damp weather. Old-time sailors anticipated a storm when knots began to tighten.

Moisture can cause music instruments to go out of tune. That's why they say that if a fiddle won't stay in tune, there's going to be a storm.

Humidex Across Canada

City	Percent chance of humidex above 30°C on July afternoon	Extreme Humidex (°C)
St. John's	9	38.6—July 6, 1983
Charlottetown	21	40.7—Aug. 22, 1976
Halifax	9	39.8—Sept. 1, 1953
Fredericton	36	44.5—July 10, 1955
Montreal	46	46.8—Aug. 1, 1975
Ottawa	41	46.0—July 1, 1955
Toronto	44	48.0—Sept. 1, 1953
Windsor	62	52.1—June 20, 1953
Winnipeg	37	45.9—Sept. 2, 1983
Regina	25	44.5—July 19, 1955
Saskatoon	18	42.0—Aug. 15, 1961
Edmonton	9	39.0—July 18, 1955
Calgary	6	36.2—July 9, 1970
Vancouver	5	37.9—July 13, 1961
Victoria	4	38.4—July 11, 1961
Whitehorse	1	32.7—May 30, 1983
Yellowknife	2	35.3—July 9, 1964

which heat exhaustion may cause nausea, dizziness and fainting. Of course, comfort is subjective and largely dependent on the age and health of the individual. Weather conditions causing prickly heat in an infant may result in heat cramps in a teenager, heat exhaustion in a middle-ager and heat stroke in a senior. Humidex is also limited as an overall hot-weather comfort index because it does not consider other factors such as pressure, wind speed, precipitation, sunshine or pollen.

Prolonged high humidities are unusual in Canada except in southern and eastern Ontario and on occasion in southeastern Manitoba and southwestern Quebec when warm, moist air pushes northward from the Gulf of Mexico and the Caribbean. Generally, humidex decreases the farther north you go. Humidex values of 45°C or more are rarely observed in Canada. Toronto, for example, has observed a humidex reading equal to or exceeding 45°C for only two hours over the past 20 years, and Ottawa only one hour. The highest humidex in Canada over

Degrees of Summer Discomfort

Humidex reading	Misery level
less than 29°C	Most people are comfortable. (Some combinations of air temperature [°C] and relative humidity [%] that produce a humidex of 29°C: 28°C and 35% relative humidity; 22°C and 90%)
30° to 39°C	People experience some discomfort. Combinations producing a 39°C humidex include 36°C and 28%; 28°C and 80%)
40° to 45°C	Great discomfort; some activities should be curtailed. (Combinations producing a 45°C humidex include 40°C and 27%; 32°C and 70%)
above 45°C	Human health is threatened by heat stroke and dehydration, and many types of physical activity should be restricted.

the past 40 years occurred at Windsor on June 20, 1953, at 3:30 p.m. At the time, the temperature was 35°C and the dew point 29°C—the humidex of 52°C was calculated years later, from recorded data.

Having a bad-hair day? It may be the humidity. The sensitivity of hair to humidity has been scientifically recognized since 1783, when a Swiss physicist, Horace de Soussure, found that hair stretches by about 2.5 percent when air goes from complete dryness to saturation. He developed the hair hygrometer for measuring atmospheric moisture. Strands of hair or a single hair are firmly supported by a mechanical linkage system that is also attached to a pen or pointer arm. As hair in the hygrometer lengthens and shortens, it moves the arm across a chart.

◄...
Performance testing shows that industrial accidents and stenographic errors increased by a third when humidity levels reached the oppressive levels.

Over the years, hygrometers have used many organic materials such as skin, sheep gut and hemp rope, but animal and human hair were found to work best. Blond or red hair were preferred, because they are even more responsive than brunette or black hair. During World War II, the U.S. War Department advertised for "blonds with hair of soft texture and the highest quality, not less than 12 inches long—all in the interest of national defense." Three hundred kilometres of blond strands were needed in humidity instruments being sent aloft in upper-air balloons. Until then, hair used in hygrometers had been imported from the Balkans.

Zookeepers report very few fatalities during heat waves, primarily because animals know what to do. Nothing!

Because hair responds very slowly at low temperatures, and not at all below –40°C, the hair hygrometer is not widely used any more. Today, most meteorologists use the psychrometer. It consists of two thermometers, one an ordinary dry bulb and the other a dry bulb wrapped in a moistened gauze sleeve. Water evaporating from around the wet bulb makes it cooler than the dry bulb. The difference in the two temperatures gives a measure of the relative humidity and dew-point temperature, which can be obtained by looking up psychrometric tables or charts.

Canadian Weather Moments

A river flows around a dam in Chicoutimi during the July 1996 Saguenay flood.
Jacques Boissinot/Canapress

WHEN IT REALLY
SNOWED IN VICTORIA

Victoria just may have Canada's most perfect climate, never too hot or too cold. It has fewer thunderstorms, milder winters and less snowfall than any other major city in Canada, even when it does snow it often melts rapidly. Some years "lotus land" does not even have a frost, let alone snow or hail. Having never experienced a tornado, and only one hurricane, Victoria quite possibly has the most benign climate anywhere in Canada. Of course Easterners are quick to ask, "But what about all that fog and rain?" Surprisingly, in an average year, Victoria has fewer foggy days and less rain than downtown Toronto.

On December 28, 1996, people in southwestern B.C. dug out from their "snowstorm of the century." Some residents who didn't own a shovel used Frisbees, dustpans, even a wok, to shovel their way out of their snowbound houses.

It is hard to find something negative about Victoria's Mediterranean mildness—with one exception. The city's average annual snowfall total, officially measured at the airport, is greater than that of the North Pole, and no city west of New Brunswick has ever had heavier daily snowfalls. Could it be true that the City of Gardens has any kind of snowfall reputation?

There is an explanation. No one really measures snowfall accumulations at the North Pole. One of the nearest weather stations is Eureka, 780 kilometres to the south. In an average year, Eureka receives 44 centimetres of snow, compared with a yearly total of 50 centimetres at Victoria International Airport. However, long-time residents of Victoria bristle at any suggestion that Environment Canada's weather station at the airport is representative of the weather some 25 kilometres to the south. The rain-shadow effect of the Olympic Mountains, the moderating effect of the Strait of Juan de Fuca and a slight urban warming results in much less snowfall downtown and in the suburbs. It is very common for snow to be falling everywhere on the inner south coast except in Victoria itself. Days with snow at the airport average 12 to 14 a year, but at weather stations downtown, only 5 or 6. As for amounts of snowfall, city stations report anywhere from one-third to one-half the airport total.

Nevertheless, despite its balmy reputation, Victoria possesses a lengthy and memory-honoured list of great snowfalls. Before systematic weather observations began at the city, there were unofficial reports of single-storm snowfalls of 61 centimetres in 1880 and 91 centimetres in 1887.

Official weather records, which began in Victoria at the Gonzales Observatory in 1898, show that Victoria is the only city in western Canada to receive more than 50 centimetres in one day. This happened three times: 53.3 centimetres on February 2, 1916, 50.8 centimetres on February 14, 1923, and 65 centimetres on December 29, 1996. The only other cities that have recorded daily snowfalls in excess of 50 centimetres are Ottawa, London, Kitchener, Quebec, St. John's and most major cities in the Maritimes.

With 196 centimetres, the winter of 1915–16 was the snowiest on record for any Victoria weather site this century—amounting to four times its normal snowfall. By the end of January, Victorians were used to winter. Temperatures had been below the freezing point for 24 consecutive days and 60 centimetres of snow lay on the ground. January had been the coldest month (a colder January did not occur until 1950).

But citizens were not to despair; February, the *Victoria Daily Colonist* predicted, would bring warmer weather. It was not to be. Instead, a perfect weather pattern for snow formed over the northwest Pacific Ocean. A strong high-pressure ridge in the Yukon and northern British Columbia pushed cold Arctic air south to Vancouver Island,

On February 3, 1916, it is estimated that 8 million tonnes of snow fell on Victoria. In that year, the city's area covered about 20 square kilometres. In 1996, the city had grown to 633 square kilometres. The record wet snowfall of 65 centimetres that fell on the city on December 27 probably weighed more than 300 million tonnes.

while a deep, low-pressure system laden with moist air was centred off-shore from Washington. Heavy rains fell across California, and the storm blanketed Nevada, Oregon, Washington and southern British Columbia. But it was in Victoria on the Saanich Peninsula that the great storm became legendary.

The snow began falling at 5 a.m. on Tuesday, February 1, and continued for 38 consecutive hours, accompanied by strong northerly winds. The wind whipped the snow into drifts up to three metres deep, and by the time the storm ended, 78.3 centimetres of new snow lay on the ground.

Although the city hired 150 men in 1916 at 40 cents an hour to shovel snow, it could only come up with 100 shovels.

For the next five days, Victoria was at a standstill. The storm buried cars and streetcars all over the city. With trains and motor traffic halted, most people who ventured out struggled through the snow on foot. A frequent scene was the single file of pedestrians clad in everything from raccoon coats and gumboots to sack-cloth leggings trudging through the snow like penguins. Women encumbered by their long skirts had a particularly difficult time getting around. The newspaper reported that a woman attired in a dashing red jacket and blue trousers with natty cuffs "caused quite a disturbance, so much so, that it is unlikely she will again make a public appearance in male attire."

Residents in the northeastern part of the city could get downtown only by taking boats and rowing to Willows Beach, where some of the roads were passable. However, up-island roads were snowed in everywhere on the Saanich Peninsula, and in some places, snowdrifts measured 60 metres long and 5 metres deep. In Victoria, horses made a comeback. The fire and police departments employed large horse-drawn sleighs, and the city engineering department used "horse power" to pull steel ploughs, fabricated especially for the storm at the city's blacksmith shop. A few farmers brought milk into the city in large cans strapped to pack horses in pioneer fashion, but most dairy farmers could only milk the cows and let the milk freeze. Some doctors rode horseback, while others donned snowshoes to get to their patients. Miraculously, no deaths or injuries were directly attributed to the storm, although hundreds suffered from exhaustion.

Most people stayed home, suspending almost all business. Those who did brave the storm to get to work ended up working at clearing sidewalks in front of their shops and offices. The post office attempted mail delivery the day after the storm, but the usual twice-a-day service was not resumed until a week later, and only to people who had cleared their sidewalks. Any retail stores that opened were deluged with telephone orders; however, only pickup orders were filled, as delivery was problematic.

Nonetheless, some businesses profited by the weather. Clothiers sold out caps and leggings, and express drivers who converted their wagons to sleighs scrambled to keep up with demand. Restaurants did a booming noon-hour business because few people went home for lunch, and hotels were filled with people who temporarily moved downtown. Among them were telephone operators summoned to handle a record 160,000 telephone calls a day—up from the usual 55,000—made by anxious relatives and friends. For some businesses, though, there were losses. One baker had 4,000 loaves he could not deliver, and fuel companies saw little profit in selling single sacks of coal.

The coal supply prior to the storm was critically low, due to the abnormally cold winter. Householders begged for coal delivery, but companies, even working late into the night and on Sunday, couldn't meet the demand. As one dealer told the *Colonist,* "The only way people can get coal is to take it home on their back." Without coal to stoke their furnaces, freezing suburbanites cut down their ornamental trees, chopped up fences and tore old houses apart for fuel. Those who lived close to the waterfront collected logs and driftwood off the beaches to burn. It was the weekend before British Columbia Electric Railway Company succeeded in opening its snow-blockaded lines.

Clearing the snow was a herculean task. Without the help of 800 to 1,000 soldiers and officers, who were training at Willows Camp, east of Victoria, it might have been weeks before the beleaguered city could get

St. John's, Newfoundland, has the distinction of 15 days with total snowfall exceeding 50 centimetres or more. Moncton is next, with five days with 50 centimetres or more.

back to normal. Soldiers cleared the rail tracks, broke trails on the streets and melted snow with pressure hoses. In one remarkable scene, a brigade of 50 husky soldiers pulled a huge wooden snowplough along a downtown thoroughfare. The newspaper reported that the human snowplough had never been seen before in Victoria, although it was a common sight on the prairies. Nine days elapsed before the first train from Victoria—an engine with a snowplough and a couple of boxcars to give it momentum—arrived in Sidney. No attempt was made to clear sidewalks or secondary streets until gangs of men unclogged main arteries and rail lines and unplugged gutters and drains. On a positive note, the blizzard proved a financial blessing for the city's unemployed. Any man or boy able to lift a shovel could make at least double the normal labourer's wages. The city gave work to all comers at 40 cents an hour. The biggest bonanza of all was shovelling snow for private home-owners and shopkeepers, who paid well above scale.

Life in Victoria was back to normal within two weeks. By February 11, the post office was making its customary two deliveries a day, and the fire department's trucks were back in action by February 13. Remarkably, the snowstorm did not even make the front-page headlines

Victoria, December 1996. Sometimes it's the only way to get around in bad weather. *Marvin Nehring/Canapress*

in the local newspaper. Today, a snowfall of any amount in Victoria usually makes front-page news across Canada.

At the end of 1996, between Christmas and New Year's, a series of brutal winter storms blasted Vancouver Island, the Lower Mainland and the Fraser Valley with more than 100 centimetres of snow. But it was the 65 centimetres of snow that fell between 10 p.m. on December 28 and 9 p.m. December 29 at the Victoria International Airport that shocked the country. The most unlikely winter city in Canada now had the distinction of having the third-highest one-day snowfall of any major city in Canada—only Fredericton and Moncton had experienced more snow in one day. In downtown Victoria, more than 80 centimetres of snow fell in the 24-hour period, easily blowing away the previous 24-hour record of 53.3 centimetres set 80 years earlier in 1916. Slightly less than 15 centimetres of snow falls on average in December at Victoria. In 1996, in the last 10 days of December, 124 centimetres of snow fell.

Major cities in Canada experiencing a daily snowfall in excess of 65 centimetres of snow (what fell in Victoria on December 28-29, 1996): St. John's (102 centimetres); Fredericton (78 centimetres); and Moncton (76 centimetres).

The amount of snow accumulation was bad enough, but high winds reduced visibility to near zero at times and piled drifts up to three metres deep. Also mixed in the snow on occasion were ice pellets that added weight and slickness to the precipitation.

If it helps, blame it on the Russians and Americans! On December 21, a pool of cold Arctic air known as the Siberian pipeline lay across most of the northwestern quadrant of North America. Temperatures plunged to −15°C in the Lower Mainland of British Columbia. Over the next week, a series of Pacific frontal storms, dubbed the Pineapple Express and packing relatively mild and very moist air, moved northeastward towards B.C. Frontal waves are fairly typical of storms that regularly strike the southern coast of the province in the fall and winter months, usually dumping copious amounts of rain. However, on this occasion, the lingering presence of the dense, deep and cold Siberian air mass plus other factors combined to produce a potentially hazardous situation. Bands of moisture collided with the entrenched Arctic air. A tug-of-war ensued, and before the frigid air could be pushed out of the region, what would normally fall as heavy rain fell instead as heavy snow and in record amounts. Within days of the snow siege, heavy rains, strong winds and temperatures rising to 11°C quickly melted the heavy snowfall, leading to serious flooding.

Damage and clean-up costs associated with the storm approached $200 million. Insurance losses amounted to about $120 million, which is the biggest pay-out in B.C. history. The true economic impact of the storm will probably never be known. The personal hardship to the million or more residents and visitors in southwestern B.C. was immeasurable.

Miraculously, there was only one report of a death. A navy lieutenant died of carbon-monoxide poisoning when snow plugged the tailpipe of his car as it was idling. Several people fell from roofs while removing snow. Some Victoria residents didn't even own a shovel or snow boots.

An army of volunteers coordinated the efforts to clear driveways and sidewalks, deliver food and needed supplies to seniors and milk formula to mothers and transport hospital staff and patients.

Victoria's airport was completely shut down, and the usually reliable B.C. ferry service, between the mainland and Vancouver Island, was cancelled, primarily because staff couldn't get to the terminals.

All modes of transportation except for track-type vehicles were brought to a standstill. Ambulance and police cars were useless, and even large firetrucks became stuck. Police officers turned to snowmobiles or just walked. The city had only five regular snowploughs. A couple of days after the huge storm, many main thoroughfares were still reduced to one lane, and side

The B.C. snowstorm in 1997 caused about $16 million in structural damage and plant loss to greenhouse operations. Losses were significant, partly because of timing—many greenhouses were gearing up for Valentine's Day. Losses were attributed to the collapse of structures as a result of snow loads, the withering of plants, the cost of additional energy to try to melt the snow as it fell and to lost wages.

streets remained impassable. Police warned residents not to come downtown. Nevertheless, hundreds of restless people drove around gawking at the mounds of snow, or searching for an open grocery store. They had no place to park, so they just left their cars in the middle of the road while they ran into the store. Police received calls about fistfights between frustrated motorists who confronted each other over right of way on one-lane streets and refused to back down. Fortunately, this type of ugliness was the exception. Stories of generosity and assistance abound. Volunteers donated food, beds and blankets to the homeless and others trapped away from home. Neighbours helped one another, and strangers pitched in to search for and rescue stranded motorists or opened their homes to storm victims.

Throughout southern Vancouver Island, roofs of schools, carports, shopping malls, stores, homes, warehouses and businesses sagged and collapsed under the crushing weight of rain-saturated snow. There were so many collapsing buildings that firefighters in some municipalities were visiting only those where people were known to be inside. Boats stored in sheds at area marinas were destroyed as the flimsy buildings fell down. Other boats moored outside simply sank under the weight of the snow, causing pollution problems. Viking Air suffered a severe blow when two of its air hangars collapsed and crushed four planes and other equipment.

On Vancouver Island, almost every greenhouse suffered damage from heavy snow loads or windows blown out by the fierce wind. About half were destroyed, as were the crops inside. Dairy farmers had to dump their milk because it could not be picked up at farms or delivered to customers.

Bakeries were forced to throw out thousands of dollars' worth of bread dough because employees could not get to work. Truckers who were stuck in towns and villages along provincial highways lost their loads. Malls and restaurants shut down for three days, as employees could not make it into work. Those who reached the workplace were exhausted by all the extra duties. Hospitals were flooded with calls from people who had not renewed their medicines and could not reach their doctors.

Victoria's "storms of the century" (separated by almost a century) dumped record amounts of snow on the city. Whereas the earlier event caused hardship to a city of 35,000, it was a mere inconvenience compared to the storm 80 years later that inflicted widespread disruption and enormous economic losses on a city and region that had grown 10 times larger. In many ways, we are much more vulnerable than our ancestors to heavy snowfalls. For certain, we have changed more than the weather has.

GREY CUP

FORECAST

The 81st Grey Cup game was played outdoors in Calgary on November 28, 1993. Originally, the fall classic was scheduled to be held inside the climate-controlled SkyDome in Toronto. But the Calgary Stampeders' owner, Larry Ryckman, guaranteed the Canadian Football League $3 million and paid the Toronto Argonauts $300,000 for the rights to play the game on the frozen turf of McMahon Stadium. His motive was to show Canadians how to stage a real Grey Cup celebration—outdoors where the game belongs.

One sure thing is that the talk in bars and hotel lobbies during Grey Cup week will always be the weather—how it's looking for Sunday's game and how to survive it. Whenever the Grey Cup is held outside, the weather overshadows the list of walking wounded and the game plan as the main topic of conversation.

Football is traditionally played on the scheduled day regardless of how adverse the weather may be or how deplorable the playing conditions. To combat the cold, teams place propane heaters on the sidelines, while players wear special clothing, from lined gloves with gripping surfaces, to fleece-lined muffs with reusable heat packs. A slippery playing surface means the right shoes must be worn at times. And even the football is affected: precipitation makes it slippery, while cold stiffens the leather.

Players manage to survive the worst that weather can bring. But for those who must pay to watch—the fans—the prospect of sitting on

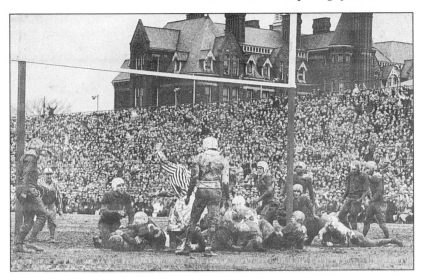

Field of mud. Grey Cup final in Winnipeg in 1950. *Glen Platt/Canapress.*

metal bleachers for up to four hours requires some ingenious preparations. The loyal wear team shirts on top of woollens and parkas or snow-mobile suits. But of course no matter what the weather, some fans are always seen in T-shirts and shorts.

Just about any kind of winter weather imaginable can occur in November, and Mother Nature—apparently not a football fan—has served up a remarkable variety of Grey Cup conditions over the years.

One of the oddest Grey Cups of all time, and in sports generally, was the famous fog bowl played in 1962 at Exhibition Stadium in Toronto. For several days, heavy fog clung to low-lying areas along Lake Ontario, reducing visibility to two metres in parts of Toronto and resulting in a rash of accidents, break-ins, purse snatchings and shopliftings. At the big game, the fog was so thick by the middle of the first quarter that spectators in the upper stands knew something was happening only by the cheers or jeers of those nearer the field. Although it was one of the greyest Grey Cups ever, it was also one of the finest ever played. That 55 points could be scored in the fog was incredible. Finally, with nine minutes and 25 seconds left on the clock, the fog got so bad that the game was stopped. It resumed the next day, with about half the Saturday crowd of 32,000 turning up for the remainder of the game—and a

28–27 win by Winnipeg over Hamilton. The game took almost 25 hours to play, the longest in Grey Cup history. It was also the first Grey Cup televised in the United States. Americans learned that Canada was more than a land of ice and snow—we were fogbound, too!

Andy O'Brien, sports editor of the now-defunct *Weekend* magazine, recalled another hard-to-see game, the 1939 Grey Cup in Ottawa. From the press box, you couldn't see plays beyond the 25-yard line through the swirling snow. Fans were asked to park their cars along the sidelines and leave their headlights on during the last quarter. The day before the game, because the gridiron was frozen solid, the grounds keepers had poured 2,000 litres of gasoline on the playing field and lit it in an attempt to burn out the frost. The strategy backfired. The flames produced pools of water that promptly refroze, leaving several good-sized rinks on the field for game day.

In the wind bowl—the 1965 Grey Cup in Toronto—a stiff gale gusting to 80 kilometres an hour at times caused punts to soar backwards. Before the game, it was agreed that because of the strong wind, all punts into the wind would automatically be whistled dead when coming in contact with receivers. Rather than have his team punt into the wind, the Winnipeg coach, Bud Grant, conceded three safety touches for a total of six points and watched his Blue Bombers lose to Hamilton by a six-point margin, 22–16.

Soggy and icy fields have had significant effects on the outcome of several games—the most memorable being the 1950 mud bowl at

Three weeks before the Grey Cup in November 1991, at the site of the Grey Cup in Winnipeg, the Edmonton Eskimos grabbed first place in the CFL's Western Division with a 28-18 victory over the Winnipeg Blue Bombers. The game took place on a field that had been reduced in size owing to ice left over from an earlier glaze storm. Instead of the usual 110 by 65 yards (100 by 59 metres), the field measured 90 by 59-1/2 yards (82 by 54.4 metres), with smaller 10-yard (9 metre) end zones. To make things worse, the temperature at game time was -13˚C, and winds gusted to 50 kilometres per hour.

Toronto's Varsity Stadium. A record single-day November snowfall of 25 centimetres the day before the game, followed by 10°C temperatures and rain on Grey Cup day, turned the uncovered field into a morass. The game was a farce. Kicks and fumbles stopped dead in the mud. When a player was tackled, he slid six or eight metres on his back while the crowd laughed. At one point, Winnipeg's Buddy Tinsley lay motionless face-down in a sea of mud. It was first thought that the tired Tinsley was unconscious and drowning. Toronto had more success controlling the slippery ball and defeated Winnipeg 13–0. Later, the Toronto quarterback, Al Dekdebrun, revealed that he had taped thumbtacks to his fingers for better ball control.

Another game at Exhibition Stadium in Toronto, in 1982, was dubbed the toilet bowl. A driving rainstorm and cold wind that blew up at half-time soaked and chilled many of the 55,000 fans and sent them into the tunnels leading to the concessions and washrooms. The conditions were so appalling that CFL officials swore Toronto would never host another Grey Cup unless they built a new stadium. Ontario's premier, William Davis, was in the stands that day, and afterwards he became a booster for a domed stadium.

Toronto Argonaut fans sadly remember Vancouver's swamp bowl of 1971, when six days of heavy rain soaked the field at Empire Stadium. With under two minutes to play and ball possession on the 11-yard line, the Toronto running back, Leon McQuay, who had fumbled only once that year, slipped and fell trying to make a turn. The ball popped loose when his elbow hit the rain-saturated carpet, stopping the Argos short in a 14–11 loss to Calgary.

In 1977, before Montreal's Olympic Stadium had a roof, heavy snow and freezing temperatures left the artificial turf so icy that both the

In the 1991 Grey Cup in Winnipeg, between the Calgary Stampeders and the Toronto Argonauts, the Argo running back Mike (Pinball) Clemons, a native of Clearwater, Florida, had his injured right foot medically frozen to allow him to play. And his healthy left foot was frozen by the elements. Said one football scribe, poor Pinball became the Snowball.

Spalding is the official supplier of footballs to the Grey Cup. The company usually provides 30 special Grey Cup footballs for the game. The balls are usually inflated to 5.9 kilograms of pressure. On extremely cold days, officials will inflate them to 6.1 kilograms in order to offset decompression from the cold. At half-time, all 30 balls are checked for inflation pressure and reinflated, if necessary.

Visitors arriving in Regina for the Grey Cup game were given a Grey Cup '95 sticker, a warm welcome and a weather update.

home-town Alouettes and the visiting Edmonton Eskimos had trouble keeping their footing. Grounds keepers applied salt to the field before game time, but not only was it ineffective, it also aggravated abrasions and burns from the artificial grass. At half-time, the wily Alouettes fired steel staples into the soles of their broomball shoes, enabling them to run, turn and outplay the Eskimos, who were using regular football cleats. The final score was 41–6. The real heroes, however, were the 68,000 fans who braved the severest wind chill of any Grey Cup: –27°C. As well, many had to walk to the stadium, owing to a Montreal transit strike.

Many games have been played on rock-hard playing fields in finger-numbing cold. The first time the Grey Cup was played in Calgary was in 1975, when –10°C temperatures combined with 27 kilometre per hour winds to produce a wind chill of –22°C. The shiver bowl was a dull affair with no touchdowns. Montreal was trailing 9–7 in the final minute, when it lined up on Edmonton's 11-yard line for what was sure to be the game-winning field goal. But Don Sweet's kick went wide because the holder's hands were too cold to hold the snap from the centre. What made the game memorable was a pre-game impromptu topless performance by a young woman who cavorted freely among the band, colour guard, game officials and dignitaries during the singing of the national anthem. It was said that she gained more yards in her romp than the entire Alouettes ground attack produced in 60 minutes of football.

Another face-numbing Grey Cup game took place in Edmonton in 1984, when Winnipeg bombed Hamilton 47–17. Fortunately, it was clear that it would be a blowout by early in the second half, and many of the 60,000 fans left to escape the bitter cold and strong winds. The first-ever Grey Cup in Winnipeg on November 24, 1991, turned out to be the coldest Grey Cup in history. The temperature at kickoff was a frigid −17.5°C. Luckily, winds were light, with plenty of sunshine.

As home of the chinook, Calgary offers better chances of having ideal weather for an outdoor game than any other Canadian CFL city. A balmy high of 16.1°C was the temperature in Calgary on November 28, 1924. On the other hand, the temperature could dip to below −26°C on the 28th, as it did in 1970, 1964, 1896 and 1897. And on Grey Cup weekend in Calgary in 1993, football fans partied in well-above-normal temperatures and plenty of sunshine. Temperatures rose to 10°C, which was pleasant compared with the previous weekend when record low −30°C air, brisk wind and snow plagued the CFL playoffs in Calgary.

With three domed stadiums in Canada, more and more Grey Cups in the future will be played in pleasant or controlled environments. Weather will no longer be an excuse, let alone the deciding factor. But football is not meant to be played in living-room comfort. Weather is part of the fun and tradition of the Grey Cup. It adds more interest, more wondrous possibilities, more strategy. Weather is what makes our Grey Cups memorable.

The 85th Grey Cup was played in Edmonton on November 16, 1997. The weather at 3:30 p.m. kickoff was −7°C, winds light from the north and northeast at 9 kilometres per hour, visibility 4 kilometres in light snow grains and fog, and ceiling 100 metres in overcast. In the lopsided game played before 60,431 bundled-up fans at below-zero Commonwealth Stadium, the Toronto Argonauts romped over the Saskatchewan Roughriders 47-23.

Grey Cup Weather Odds*

	Montreal	Ottawa	Toronto	Hamilton	Winnipeg	Regina	Edmonton	Calgary	Vancouver
Game time temperature below −15°C	−	−	−	−	17:1	10:1	10:1	18:1	−
Game time temperature below 0°C	3:1	2.5:1	6:1	11:1	1.3:1	1.5:1	2:1	2.5:1	59:1
Game time temperature above 0°C	1.4:1	1.5:1	1.2:1	1.1:1	4:1	3:1	2:1	1.5:1	1:1
Day with 5 cm or more of snow	13:1	13:1	30:1	58:1	23:1	52:1	26:1	37:1	200:1
Day with 2 cm or more of snow	6:1	6:1	12.5:1	23:1	8:1	9:1	10:1	11:1	45:1
Day with rainfall	4.3:1	5:1	5:1	3.5:1	43:1	66:1	111:1	125:1	2:1
Day with any precipitation	2.5:1	2.5:1	3.3:1	3:1	5.3:1	5:1	5.5:1	8:1	2:1

* Based on records this century

THE YEAR OF WEATHER DISCONTENT

In 1996, Canada suffered through some of the most extreme and destructive weather ever to hit the country. For most of the year, the weather either froze, buried, soaked, buffeted or frightened us. No part of the land seemed to escape the wrath of the weather gods in 1996.

It was truly the stuff of a Hollywood catastrophe film—a raging storm on Vancouver Island, hailers on the Prairies, deluges of biblical proportion in Quebec. Three drive-in theatres were heavily damaged by tornadoes and, yes, they were about to show *Twister*.

The outbursts of extreme and freakish weather made the year by far and away the most expensive for Canada's property and casualty insurers. Most of the financial fallout stemmed from flooding in Quebec's Saguenay region—Canada's $1 billion disaster—but multi-million-dollar hailstorms hit Winnipeg and Calgary; flash flooding occurred in Ottawa and Montreal; and severe thunderstorms in Ontario, Saskatchewan and Alberta also took their toll.

Total property damage, much of it uninsured, exceeded $1.5 billion. Indirect costs and losses from revenue shortfall, cancelled events, missed opportunities and slowed business was a $3 billion hit to the Canadian economy.

Remarkably, though, the number of personal injuries and fatalities linked to weather incidents was relatively low. Unofficial numbers point to fewer than 25 weather-related deaths (excluding deaths from road accidents and hypothermia)—10 from flooding in the Saguenay and 6 from lightning in separate incidents.

The weather news was not all bad. Canada had fewer bad-air days and fewer trees were consumed by forest fires compared with 1995. And Statistics Canada estimated 1996–97 Canadian grains and oilseeds production at a record of about 67 million tonnes, 14 percent above 1995–96 and 18 percent above the 10-year average.

The year 1996 entered the record books as one of wettest in the 20th century. Nationally, it was the wettest year in the 49-year period since comparable precipitation records began in 1948. There was about 11 percent more precipi-

In the latter half of January, it was colder in most cities in western and central Canada than it was at the North Pole. Geraldton's all-time record low of -50.2°C on January 31, 1996, was the coldest temperature recorded anywhere in Ontario in more than 37 years. Calgary endured its longest uninterrupted cold snap in nearly four decades. And Winnipeg broke its record for the longest cold snap in history, when overnight temperatures stayed below -30°C for 19 days.

The Saguenay River floodwaters cut off a downtown Chicoutimi street.. *Jacques Boissinot/Canapress*

tation than normal, although some southern areas such as the Prairies and British Columbia were drier than usual. It was especially wet in spring and fall in the agricultural areas of southern British Columbia, the Prairies and the lower Great Lakes. The national average temperature for 1996 was near normal, representing a cool change from the previous three years. This was the result of a slightly cooler-than-average winter and spring and a cooler fall.

While Canada contributed some coolness to the global average temperature, figures compiled by NASA for land and ocean areas around the world showed the period January 1996 to December 1996 to be 0.31°C warmer than the average. Although 1996 was cooler than 1995's all-time record warmth, the earth still experienced its fourth-warmest year in 131 years.

In Winnipeg, when the wind chill temperature hit -65°C, mail carriers were excused from walking their routes for the first time in memory.

Spring 1996 in Canada interrupted a string of six consecutive warm springs when temperatures averaged about –0.3°C below normal. The spring was the third wettest in 49 years.

Of some surprise, summer averaged about 0.5°C warmer than normal. Eight of the past 10 years were warmer and wetter than normal.

Among the weather records of significance in 1996 were:
- The wettest growing season on record in parts of southwestern Ontario; wettest April to July in parts of southern Ontario since record keeping began 157 years ago
- The coolest, cloudiest May on record and the dullest May, June and July ever in Edmonton
- The wettest April ever in Vancouver and Victoria; the wettest April to July in 157 years in Toronto
- The wettest July ever in Halifax
- The sunniest August on record in Ottawa
- The rainiest and gloomiest April on record for much of British Columbia
- The dullest May, June and July ever in cental Alberta

According to one entomologist from the University of Guelph, the frequency of bug bites in southern Ontario was 40 percent above those of 1995.

The top 10 weather stories of 1996, ranked according to total estimated losses:

1. The Saguenay Flood. By far the worst catastrophe of the year was the flooding and mud slides in Quebec's Saguenay River valley in mid-July. The storm produced the largest overland deluge in Canada this century—an amount equivalent to a two-month flow over Niagara Falls—triggering a surge of water, rocks, trees and mud that killed 10 people and forced 12,000 residents to flee their homes. It was the deadliest flood since Hurricane Hazel in Toronto in 1954.

   The scale of the tragedy was staggering. Many of the region's roads and bridges and delivery systems for power and water simply disappeared. To the insurance industry, it was Canada's worst-ever weather disaster in economic losses. By including insured and uninsured losses and indirect costs to the economy, total losses are sure to exceed $1.5 billion.

2. High Energy Costs. In much of Canada, 1996 featured one of the longest and most vicious winters in recent memory. Three straight weeks of frigid weather gripped almost the entire country in January, making it colder in most cities in western and central

Canada than it was at the North Pole. The extreme cold created additional hardship for the homeless in Canadian cities. To keep up with the cold, utility companies pumped out power in record amounts from British Columbia to New Brunswick. It cost Canadians an additional $500 million to keep their dwellings as comfortable as in winter 1995.

3. Costly Prairie Hailstorms. In July, hailstones the size of fists bombarded Winnipeg and Calgary, racking up close to $300 million in property losses. In Manitoba, more than half the losses were for auto damage, making it the worst single-disaster claim against the Manitoba Public Insurance Corporation in its 25-year history. At least a third of the cars damaged had to be written off. Calgary was pummelled twice in July by major hailstorms. Entire streets were littered with branches and broken shingles, cars were pounded, windows smashed and siding ripped off houses. Along with the hail came drenching rains that flooded neighbourhoods, submerged hundreds of cars and knocked out the city's 911 service.

No statistic better describes spring/summer across much of Canada in 1996 than the frequency of wet and dry weekends. At Toronto, for example, wet/dry weekends between April 1 and mid-July numbered 13 and 2 respectively. However, between July 20 and September 2, there was not a single wet Saturday and Sunday in seven weekends.

4. Wet and Cold Weather Reduces Crop Yields. During much of the growing season, Canadian farmers wondered whether they would ever get the heat they needed. In August, hot, dry and sunny weather finally arrived. Unfortunately for western Canadian farmers, prospects in early September for one of the most bountiful grain crops in Canadian history didn't materialize. Fall temperatures across the West were much below normal—the Prairies had their second-coldest fall in half a century—and precipitation was much above normal—the seventh wettest fall in about 50 years. For Canadian western red spring wheat, which represents 80 percent

of western spring wheat production, cool wet weather meant a reduction in grade, denying farmers an additional $180 million.

In southern Ontario, winter wheat production was severely affected by the wet cool weather throughout the growing season. Record rainfall resulted in the worst outbreak of blight fungus ever seen in Ontario. According to Agriculture Canada, the excessive moisture and disease not only reduced yields, but it also reduced the quality of most of the crop to feed, since affected grain cannot be used for human consumption. The loss was estimated to be about $90 million.

On April 20, a twister near Williamsford, Ontario, plucked a 78-year-old man from the kitchen of his trailer and flung him 150 metres into a field. He recalled opening a can of soup, hearing the storm, then seeing splintering glass. Next he remembers crawling in the field, spitting dirt and looking for his glasses and false teeth.

5. Deep Winter Snows. So much snow fell early in the winter that before 1996 even started, many cities in western and central Canada had all but exhausted their snow-removal budgets. Hardest hit was the central Ontario snow belt from Barrie to Sault Ste. Marie, where on several occasions, cars disappeared in snowdrifts, service centres became refugee camps, roofs collapsed and schools closed. On at least one occasion, officials declared the Muskoka region a disaster area; even snowploughs and police cruisers were taken off the roads.

Insurance claims paid in the first three months of 1996 were 11 percent higher than the winter before, when the weather was much less severe. Total insured losses owing to the weather were estimated at $165 million.

6. Slow Spring Affects Retail Sales. For most of Canada, the winter season gave way to the monsoon season. Unrelenting rains and dreary weather plagued the country from April to June. Farming operations were consistently two to four weeks late. Garden centres and golf courses were virtually empty during the spring.

Retailers blamed the persistent cool and rainy weather for a 30 percent drop in the sales of weather-related goods and services, such as pools, air conditioners and warm-season apparel. Sales of general merchandise in April and June were down by $100 million over the previous year.

A farmer near Chatham, Ontario, was at home watching TV on July 7 when a severe thunderstorm sprang up. Seconds after he got up to close a window, the chimney crashed through the ceiling, flattening his empty chair and sending it through the floor into a crawlspace. The storm tore off roofs, uprooted trees and sucked windows and screens from their frames.

7. Flash Flooding in Ottawa and Montreal. The third major storm in less than two weeks, and the worst on record, hit Ottawa-Hull in early August with 100 to 150 millimetres in 90 minutes. Total insured property damage exceeded $20 million, not including the cost of repairs to damaged sewers and roads. The city received more than 800 calls from residents with flooded basements and other water problems, about the number reported over the past 10 years.

Between November 7 and 9, 30 hours of steady rains drenched parts of southwestern Quebec. The rains washed out sections of highway, collapsed bridges, derailed trains and undermined road and rail beds. About 1,000 residents south of the St. Lawrence River were driven from their homes, and another 5,000 reported flooded basements. Damage estimates put the event well in excess of $50 million.

8. Severe Thunderstorms and Tornadoes. The snow had hardly melted in southern Ontario when the season's first tornadoes tore through regions east of Lake Huron in April. The twisters injured two people and killed livestock; crushed dozens of houses, barns and trailers; ripped apart electrical power lines and scattered glass everywhere. Total property losses, much of it uninsured, approached $8 million.

Severe thunderstorms on July 4 spawned at least eight tornadoes in Saskatchewan along with winds of 140 km/h and hail the size of golf balls. The strong winds blew roofs off and knocked down 20 steel towers carrying the main transmission lines for Saskatoon. Property damage was about $15 million. Two weeks later, the worst outbreak of tornadoes in Alberta in 10 years tore a swath of destruction from Coronation to Swan Hills. Seven tornadoes touched down, trashing trailers and flattening granaries to the tune of $10 million. Near Stoney Plain, more than 100 millimetres of rain fell in severe thunderstorms, backing up sewers and flooding dozens of basements for another $10 million in losses. Tornado-related damage in Canada easily exceeded $50 million. Miraculously, there were only a handful of injuries and no deaths.

9. Spring Flooding. Significant flooding occurred in several communities across Canada during much of the spring and early summer. Ice-choked rivers fed by melting snow and ice and spring rains turned streets into rivers and fields into lakes. The Okanagan experienced its worst flooding in six years; and in southern Saskatchewan, ice jams caused several rivers to overflow, forcing the evacuation of 100 families and drowning several cattle. In late April, the Red River inundated farm fields, roads and major highways south of Winnipeg, leading authorities to declare a provincial flood disaster for the first time since 1979. In Timmins, Ontario, the Mattagami River overflowed its banks in the worst flooding in 36 years.

Damage figures for spring flooding across Canada range between $20 and $50 million.

10. Hurricanes and Weather Bombs. Four hurricane-force storms struck eastern Canada in

Calgary was pounded by the second severe hail and rainstorm in eight days on July 24. Orange-size hail clogged storm sewers and caused massive flooding. Drivers were marooned on the roofs of their vehicles. Attendants at a gas station turned down $50 bribes from motorists wanting to shelter vehicles in the service bays. One attendant watched about 20 vehicles attempt to jam underneath the pump canopy to avoid hail damage.

1996: Bertha, Edouard, Fran and Hortense. On September 14, Hurricane Hortense swept east of Halifax and traversed western Newfoundland, the first hurricane to achieve landfall in Canada in 21 years. Winds topped 161 km/h on Cape Breton Island, strong enough to fell trees, lift roofs and blow out windows. To make matters worse, the storm arrived at high tide, producing a huge surf. Total property losses approached $5 million.

The year was the second consecutive season with above-average hurricane formation in the North Atlantic. In 1996 there were 13 named storms, of which 9 were hurricanes, including 6 intense ones, compared with a normal of 9 storms, 6 hurricanes and 2 intense ones.

Described as the worst storm since Typhoon Freda in 1962, a weather bomb struck Vancouver Island on October 17, causing massive power outages and felling trees, setting adrift 50 pleasure boats and ripping apart docks. A weather bomb is a marine storm that intensifies very quickly and moves faster than a hurricane. This storm packed winds as strong as 161 km/h and produced waves as high as 30 metres. More than 23,000 people on Vancouver Island were without electricity for hours. Final cost figures for insured property damages exceeded $1 million.

A band of severe weather swept across north-central Alberta on August 2, dousing campgrounds, smashing windshields and snapping trees. Mud-slicked grounds made walking and dancing at the Big Valley Jamboree in Camrose even more hazardous than usual. The 300 or so members of the Western Canadian Association for Nude Recreation had to huddle in tents rather than worship the sun.

So are the number of weather-related disasters in Canada and around the world increasing? The Insurance Bureau of Canada says that ever since the Edmonton tornado of 1987, the number of multi-million-dollar losses from weather disasters has been on the rise in Canada. Around

Table of Top 10 Weather Events in 1996

Number	Event	Estimated Losses
1	The Saguenay flood (Quebec)	$1.5 billion
2	High energy costs (Canada-wide)	$500 million
3	Prairie hailstorms (Winnipeg and Calgary)	$300 million
4	Reduced crop yields (Prairies and Ontario)	$270 million
5	Deep winter snows (central Ontario)	$165 million
6	Slow spring affects retail sales (Canada-wide)	$100 million
7	Flash flooding (Ottawa and Montreal)	$70 million
8	Severe thunderstorms and tornadoes (Prairies and Ontario)	$50 million
9	Spring flooding (western and central Canada)	$20-$50 million
10	Hurricanes and weather bombs (East and West Coasts)	$5 million

the world, insurers have witnessed over the past 20 years a fourfold increase in the number of weather catastrophes. More worrisome, costs from natural disasters have risen tenfold during the same period. Before 1987, there was not a single natural disaster with damages exceeding $1 billion anywhere in the world, but since then there have been at least 18 such disasters.

Although many climatologists in Canada found the outbursts of extreme and freakish weather interesting, they weren't generally surprised by the unusual weather patterns. By its very nature, weather is chaotic and turbulent, and extremes, especially in Canada, are a normal feature of the climate. Climatologists are, however, becoming increasingly concerned that the volatile weather of 1996 may have been just a dry run of what we may expect much more of from now on, given rampant climate change. Perhaps Canada's relative good fortune in avoiding natural catastrophes, which have plagued other countries, may be running out.

North America's Coldest Day

On February 3, 1947, at 7:20 a.m. Yukon time, the weather observer Gordon Toole hurried the 30 metres from the warm, log barracks at Snag Airport, Yukon, to the weather-instrument compound next to the runway. For eight straight days the temperature had been below –58°F (–50°C), but on this morning it felt colder. Toole could plainly hear the dogs barking at the village six kilometres to the north, and his exhaled breath made a tinkling sound as it fell to the ground in a white powder. His six husky dogs were really feeling the cold. They were asleep on top of their kennels, curled up with their noses tucked right up under their tails to garner every calorie of heat.

By the time he arrived at the white-louvered shelter housing the thermometers, he could feel the cold seeping through his parka. He unlatched the door of the instrument shelter and shone the flashlight inside, but was careful not to lean forward and breathe on the thermometers. He saw something that he had never seen before: the tiny sliding scale inside the glass thermometer column had fallen into the bulb at the end, well below the –80°F (–62.2°C) point—the last mark on the thermometer.

Toole rushed back to the barracks where he coaxed his colleague, Wilf Blezard, to return to the instrument compound. Using a set of dividers to measure the tiny bit of alcohol left in the column, Toole estimated the temperature to be about –83°F (–63.9°C). As he dutifully scratched a mark on the outside of the thermometer sheath adjacent to the end of the alcohol, he thought about what the Department of Transport head office had advised three days earlier. If the alcohol level ever fell below –80°F, they should mark a corresponding point on the thermometer sheath with a pen. Typical advice from Toronto, Toole thought: ink does not flow at that temperature. Instead, he made the historic mark using a fine, sharp file.

To complete the job, the observers noted the weather was a repeat of the past two months—clear, dry and calm. Snow on the ground amounted to 38 centimetres, but was evaporating at 3 centimetres a day.

The visibility at eye level was 30 kilometres; however, on February 3, ground visibility was greatly reduced. At about arm's length, an eerie, dull grey shroud of patchy ice fog hung above the dogs and heated buildings.

Back inside the Snag weather office, the Department of Transport radio operator transmitted the weather observation to Whitehorse and Toronto. Within the hour, the director of the Canadian Weather Service congratulated Snag on becoming North America's "cold pole." He also asked Toole to send the thermometer back to be recalibrated. The two observers shared the news with the rest of the camp before packing the thermometer for air shipment to Toronto to have the readings confirmed.

But almost a week passed before it was warm enough for an airplane to land at Snag. Once in Toronto, the thermometer was put through several laboratory tests before technicians concluded that it had been reading about 1.6°F (0.9°C) in error. Three months later, the weather service accepted a value of −81.4°F (−63°C) as the corrected temperature—still the lowest official temperature ever recorded in North America. It is a record that still stands today—more than 50 years later.

At Snag that day, all 16 airport employees did not need confirmation in Toronto. They could feel how cold it was. Still, they were excited by the news. Blezard, now retired in Grande Prairie, Alberta, recalls, "We had to put a little lock on the door to the instrument screen because everybody was rushing out and looking at the thermometers. Even the slightest bit of body heat would cause the alcohol to jump." Fifty years is a long time ago, so perhaps it is not surprising that Toole's memories of the day are different. "Staff interest," he said, "was pretty limited. There was no euphoria, prolonged celebrating or serious discussion on how to commemorate the moment."

Perhaps no one understood the historic significance, or maybe it was just that the cold showed no sign of abating. But that was to change. By 2 p.m., the day's high reached a relatively balmy −54°F (−47.8°C). Before the day was over, media from around the world had besieged the "frozen chosen" for exclusive interviews on the historic cold. Writers from the *Milwaukee Journal* and *Vancouver Sun* phoned for front-page stories to learn what −80°F felt like. The *Globe and Mail* carried the

Within Canada, Quebec is the coldest province and Nova Scotia the warmest.

Quebec	**-2.6°C**
Manitoba	**-2.3°C**
Newfoundland-	
Labrador	**0.1°C**
Saskatchewan	**0.1°C**
Ontario	**0.5°C**
Alberta	**0.6°C**
British Columbia	**3.4°C**
New Brunswick	**4.3°C**
Prince Edward	
Island	**5.5°C**
Nova Scotia	**6.2°C**
Yukon	**-5.6°C**
Northwest	
Territories	**-11.3°C**

following headline: "Snag snug as mercury [sic] sags to a record −82.6°." The thermometers did not use mercury because it freezes at −39°F (−39°C). They were alcohol thermometers and the newspaper's reporter, although not the headline writer, knew it. Later in the story: "The only reason the men didn't celebrate was that all the alcohol at the station was in the thermometer and that was nearly frozen."

Telegrams of congratulations arrived from many countries. But some experts expressed scepticism. For British meteorologists, who at that time measured coldness in degrees of frost, upward of 115 degrees of frost was just too much to comprehend. (Degrees of frost refer to the number of degrees the temperature falls below the freezing point of 32°F [0°C].)

On February 8, a plane arrived at Snag with American military and media who wanted to learn what it was like living and working in such cold conditions. The men at Snag, however, were more interested in the visitors' cargo of meat, beer and rye than in becoming celebrities to strangers. Hearing from family and friends was different. "We were celebrities to them," remembered Toole. "And finally, they could locate Snag on the map of North America."

Why is the lowest temperature record one of the best-remembered Canadian weather records? First, it was for that typically Canadian feature: cold. Second, it was the record for the Western world. And finally, the short, odd name "Snag" made this legend of frigidity live on.

Snag was named during the Klondike gold rush. Because boatmen could not read the silty waters of nearby stretches of the White River and its tributaries, boats had to be poled going upstream. On occasion, they would be "snagged" and punctured by sharp pointed tree trunks submerged below the milky waters, hence the name. A long-time Yukon resident, Jean Gordon, of Mayo, about 300 kilometres northeast of Snag, knows many hunters who have lost all their supplies, guns and meat when a snag speared their boat. She explains that snags come from

trees that have washed down from riverbanks during high water. They move downstream with the heavy butt and root end sinking and the treetop facing downstream. As the water recedes, the butt will become anchored to the stream bed and the rest of the tree will oscillate in the water. As the limbs become denuded, a long snag pointed downstream, which can move up and down in the current, creates a very dangerous hazard, especially for boats travelling upstream with the snag below the surface. Experienced rivermen can read the water even when it is muddy or full of silt, but they hate waters where there are snags.

◄ ....

The number of Canadians who head south every winter is four million—10 percent travel to Hawaii; 10 percent to Arizona; 20 percent to the Caribbean; and 60 percent to Florida.

The Snag weather station operated from 1943 to 1966. It was located at the Snag Airport, east of the Alaska-Yukon boundary, and 25 kilometres north of the Alaska Highway at Mile 1178. The airport was at coordinates 62°23'N and 140°23'N, with an elevation of 646 metres. Set in a broad, bowl-shaped, north-south valley of the White River, a tributary of the Yukon River, the now-abandoned airport was surrounded by unglaciated uplands of moderate relief. The vegetation was mostly scrub and poplar trees about 3 to 6 metres tall. The magnificent St. Elias mountains lay 50 kilometres to the south. The tiny village of Snag, consisting of less than a dozen people, was 6 kilometres to the north of the airport, near the point where the Snag Creek flowed into the White River.

Of the 16 staff members at Snag airport, four single men in their early twenties were there to observe the weather. Toole was the officer in charge of the weather station. Meteorological staff earned about $1,320 annually, with an extra $20 monthly isolation allowance, which covered the room rate in the barracks. The daily food charge was $0.50.

The other airport employees were radio operators, also employed by the Department of Transport, and airport maintenance and operations personnel, employed by the Royal Canadian Air Force (RCAF), whose main job was to keep the runway open. Incidentally, in winter this meant compacting the snow, not ploughing or blowing the strip bare.

Here's a quick way of calculating wind chill temperature. Take half the wind speed (km/h), make the result a negative value and add it to the air temperature. For example, if the wind speed is 30 km/h and air temperature is -10°C, then half the wind speed is 15, make it -15, and add it to the temperature (-15 + -10 = -25°C). The wind chill temperature is -25°C.

Snag was part of the Northwest Staging Route—one of several emergency landing strips or observing stations through northwest Canada connecting Yukon and Alaska with central Canada and the United States. They were set up in 1942 and 1943 to provide basic weather services for the RCAF, the United States Army Air Force and civilian aviation companies providing military transport. Most pilots flying the northwest route had to fly with visual contact with the ground, called visual flight rules (VFR); otherwise, they might get lost. If weather socked in the main airports, the pilots used alternative airports like Snag and Smith River.

The continental climate in this part of Yukon resembles that of eastern Siberia. Yearly precipitation averages 339 millimetres, with nearly two-thirds of that falling between May and September. The average annual snowfall totals 155 centimetres. Winds are light with, in winter, a large percentage of calms. Temperatures are more variable with prolonged cold winters and warm summers. The January average daytime high is –13.2°F (–25.1°C) and the average nighttime low –32.1°F (–35.6°C); comparable July averages are high, 69.6°F (20.9°C), and, low 44.6°F (7°C).

The winter of 1946–47 had been exceptionally cold in the Canadian northwest. At Snag, temperatures dipped below –58°F (–50°C) on 6 days in December, and on 11 days in January. From January 27 to

February 5, temperatures remained below –67°F (–55°C). On January 30, the temperature fell to –76°F (–60°C), giving Yukon its coldest day ever, and Canada, its lowest in 38 years. On February 2, the temperature fell to –80°F (–62.2°C) which was a new all-time Canadian record cold. But it was to last only a day: the very next day, the corrected temperature was –81°F (–62.8°C)—a new record low for all of North America.

The cold was not confined to Snag. Temperatures reached their lowest point between February 1 and 3 throughout Yukon. Among the coldest sites were Aishihik Airport, –70.1°F (–56.7°C); Dawson, –72.9°F (–58.3°C); Haines Junction, –63.0°F (–52.8°C); Kluane Lake, –56.0°F (–48.9°C); Teslin, –52.1°F (–46.7°C); Watson Lake, –67.0°F (–55°C); and Whitehorse, –59.1°F (–50.6°C).

"The wind blows so hard the birds fly backwards. ... We can't even get our seasons right. Spring lasts about four days. Summer means forest fires, floods and flies. We get most of our sunshine in the winter—between noon and two."— Pam Buckway, CBC radio host writing about Yukon

On February 3, the thermometer at Fort Selkirk, a very small community on the Yukon River, 180 kilometres east-northeast of Snag, recorded –85°F (–65°C), corrected for instrument error. This reading, however, was not considered official because the thermometer was exposed on the outside wall of a building and not housed in the standard instrument shelter. That same day at the station at Mayo, the temperature apparently reached –80°F (–62.2°C). "Apparently" because at midnight on February 15, the station burned down, destroying the weather instruments and observation records. Nevertheless, photographic evidence exists that shows Mayo's temperature reading on that day, about –80°F, just marginally above the Snag low. Mayo booster Jean Gordon claims that while Snag can claim a lower temperature extreme, Mayo, with its two schools, hotels and population of 500 people, can boast being the coldest "decent-sized" community in North America and, as a road sign entering Mayo asserts, the town with the largest temperature range: a huge 177 degrees, from a maximum of 97.0°F (36.1°C) to a minimum of –80°F (–-62.2°C).

How did such cold happen? As in most Arctic cold spells, weather conditions in 1946–47 were favourable for a steep temperature inversion. Inversions, a frequent feature of Arctic winters, are exceptions to the general rule that temperature decreases with increasing altitude. Inversions can be produced by gravitational drainage of cold air or by radiation. In elevated terrain, the heavy, dense air sinks and slides down the mountain slopes, often pushing any warmer air aloft. The ground also grows colder by radiating heat to the cloud-free sky. In doing so, the ground readily cools the air immediately above it, especially when the skies are clear, there is unlimited visibility and the winds are calm or light. A layer of air closest to the ground may be as much as 20 to 40 degrees colder than the air at 1,000 metres.

In 1946–47, a strong westerly circulation across North America confined cold Arctic air over Alaska and northwestern Canada for much of the winter. During this time, the cold dome of heavy, dense air over Yukon intensified. With a continuous supply of cold air from northeastern Siberia, the cold dome over Yukon grew in extent and severity, creating all the record lows. But a dramatic change was to occur later in February: the westerlies relaxed, the cold air spilled through to eastern North America, resulting in severe cold as far south as Florida, and brought maritime air from the Pacific to southern Yukon, where the cold broke for a few days. At Snag, the temperature even rose to a more civilized 45°F (7°C).

How did −81.4°F (−63°C) feel? Most Canadians never experience temperatures lower than −50°F (−45.6°C). Blezard and Toole repeatedly said there was a considerable difference between −50°F and −80°F.

The following anecdotes, pieced together from station correspondence with the regional office in Edmonton that winter, as well as from recent interviews and correspondence with the two observers, give us a glimpse of what life was like for the frozen 16 at Snag during the winter of 1946–47. Says Blezard: "An aircraft that flew over Snag that day at 10,000 feet [3,050 metres] was first heard when over 20 miles [32 kilometres] away; and later, when overhead, still at 10,000 feet, the engine roar was deafening. It woke everyone who was sleeping at the time, because they thought the airplane was landing at the airport."

Anyone who has ever skated outside or gone for long walks in the dead of winter knows that the colder it gets, the farther sound carries. That is because sound ordinarily spreads obliquely upward over our heads and is therefore not heard very far away. But in very cold, stable air, the inversion bends the sound waves back towards the earth, where they tend to hug the ground. Furthermore, audibility is improved by the absence of turbulence or wind. In the end, conversations usually heard 30 metres away can be heard more than a kilometre away if the air is clear.

However, at temperatures below –58°F (–50°C), ice fog reduces the transmission of sound waves considerably. Here is an excerpt from a letter the officer-in-charge at Mayo, Matthew H. "Harry" Ewing, wrote on March 8, 1947, to Dr. Andrew Thomson, director of the Meteorological Branch in Toronto. In it, he commented about a friend of his, a trapper and prospector in the hills north of Mayo, who claimed that ice fog definitely kills sound, whereas severe cold without fog is very favourable for conducting sound: "Once the old-timer was working across a valley 3 or 4 miles [5 kilometres] from another party. The valley was filled with fog at 60°F below [–51.1°C] but there was no fog on the mountains. In the very cold air, when the men across the valley were chopping wood and making other noises around camp, he could hear them very clearly, much clearer than normally."

At such temperatures, there are even extraordinary sounds: for instance, staff at Snag could not only see but also hear their moist breath solidify to ice outside, in a hissing or faint swishing sound. A piece of thin ice, when broken, sounded exactly like breaking glass. From his home in Watson Lake, Yukon, Toole recalled: "Ice in the White River about a mile east of the airport, cracked and boomed loudly, like gunfire. During the bitter cold, you would go days without seeing any wildlife, apart from ravens, rabbits, mice, snowbirds and ptarmigans. Cold air generated intense radio static much like the crackling during a thunderstorm."

There were other cold-weather experiences mentioned by the observers at Snag. For days, a small fog or steam patch would appear over the sled dogs, at a height of six metres. It would disappear only in the warm part of the day when the temperature warmed up to –60°F (–51.1°C). A chunk of ice was so cold that when brought into a warm room, it took five full minutes before there was any trace of moisture, even when held in the hand.

Blezard recalls antics around the camp during the cold spell: "We threw a dish of water high into the air, just to see what would happen. Before it hit the ground, it made a hissing noise, froze and fell as tiny round pellets of ice the size of wheat kernels. Spit also froze before hitting the ground. Ice became so hard the axe rebounded from it. At such temperatures, metal snapped like ice; wood became petrified; and rubber was just like cement. The dogs' leather harness couldn't bend or it would break."

Toole added a few other memories of the cold snap: "It was unique to see a vapour trail several hundred yards long pursuing one as he moved about outside. Becoming lost was of no concern. As an observer walked along the runway, each breath remained as a tiny, motionless mist behind him at head level. These patches of human breath fog remained in the still air for three to four minutes, before fading away. One observer even found such a trail still marking his path when he returned along the same path 15 minutes later."

At –0˚C, sound travels 331 metres in one second; at 21˚C, it travels 344 metres per second

Life in the cold had its complications. Surprisingly, heating the log buildings was less of a problem than one might expect. In a memo to his superior, Dr. Tom How, officer-in-charge of the Edmonton forecast office, Toole wrote about the hardships that winter:

> With constant stoking of the furnace the temperature of the barracks remained quite comfortable. The only uncomfortably cool room in the barracks was the common room, this was due to a large hole, 8 feet by 4 feet [2.5 by 1 metre], being in the ceiling. The hole was caused by the freezing and bursting of one of the water pipes on December 2nd. Despite promises by the RCAF at Whitehorse that a carpenter was coming up on the first available aircraft to fix the ceiling, the temporary patch, put on by two of the radio personnel and myself, remains....
>
> No provisions have been made for supplying the barracks

with water for drinking or washing purposes. This, as you can see, has made it almost impossible for personnel to wash more than once a day and has terminated showers or baths. These unsanitary conditions will very likely continue until such time as the RCAF are prevailed upon to haul water by truck. After seconds outdoors, nose hairs froze rigidly and your eyes tear. Facial hair and glasses become thickly crusted with frozen breath … you had to be careful not to inhale too deeply for fear of freezing or scalding one's lungs. The only other discomfort caused by the cold were numerous cases of beginning frostbite, particularly the familiar "ping" as the tip of one's nose froze. One only had to remain outside for 3 or 4 minutes with face exposed before cheeks, nose and ears were frozen.

In a letter to me dated August 22, 1995, Toole claimed that the crew had first-class toilet facilities when the indoor plumbing froze up. "A small building was hauled about 100 feet [30 metres] from the barracks. It boasted four seating positions, but best of all, a wood heater that was kept stoked at all times. Talk about comfort!"

During the extreme cold, outdoor chores had to be postponed. The weather staff felt fortunate that observing duties kept them outside only for two minutes every hour. On the other hand, the enlisted men were outside for relatively long bouts, hauling wood to keep the barracks, the garage and the powerhouse warm. They had to take extra precautions to prevent throat and lung burn from overexertion in the frigid air. Says Blezard, "It was easy to freeze your nose at −70°F [−56.7°C] without even knowing it was cold. At −30°F [−34.4°C] you feel it coming."

Beating the "cold blues" was another challenge. Toole busied himself during the cold spell by checking his trap lines; others played poker or hearts, boxed, listened to classical music, read or talked. And the talk was about the wretched cold. According to Blezard, "When the cold stayed for just a few days, it didn't bother you that much. It was something to talk about, and probably improved the state of mind for a while. But the enduring cold wore you down by sapping your energy."

In the midst of the cold spell, there was no resupply by RCAF planes from Whitehorse for several weeks. Aircraft did not fly when the tem-

"Besides the two horses ... sled dogs, there were ravens, rabbits, and ptarmigan trying to survive the cold. Many mice also sought refuge in our warm buildings. The janitor had a large tomcat, so the poor unfortunate mice didn't fare so well! Needless to say, the cat was very happy and well fed! The horses, with their two-to-three-inch buildup of snow and ice on their hoofs, didn't seem to suffer from the cold, and our cook found it in his heart to feed them a variety of "snacks," i.e., weiners, peelings, crusts of bread, etc....

(continued)

perature fell below −50°F (−45.6°C). The pilots might get the planes started after several hours, but could not get them warm enough to take off. Furthermore, the pilots were afraid the landing gear would freeze up and crack. Explained Toole: "In the extreme cold the aircraft would land, but the pilots learned never to use their brakes for long intervals, as they froze up and could not be broken loose until warmed. As a result, the practice was for the aircraft to taxi slowly up to the unloading area, where items were thrown out as the aircraft continued to move. It was extremely cold for the personnel unloading in the prop wash and not the safest, but it worked."

Blezard recalled: "All we ate was fish and bacon and eggs ... There was very little meat ... We lived mostly on beans for the last five days." So the men were very happy when the cold spell ended and the first airplane (a DC3) could land, bringing meat, vegetables and fruit, a few cases of beer and a couple of bottles of rye.

Starting machinery was also a chore. And getting an engine started was no guarantee it would continue to run. At that temperature, the oil and the transmission fluid coagulated into something approaching a solid. In addition, truck tires could splay open when they hit ruts. But the weather instruments, apart from the thermometers, all seemed to work in the cold.

How does the Snag record stand compared with the rest of North America? It beat the previous lowest Canadian temperature of −77.9°F (−61.1°C), recorded on January 11, 1911, at Fort Vermilion, Alberta (still western Canada's lowest official temperature), as well as the lowest temperature ever recorded in the United States.

That was −79.8°F (−62.1°C) recorded on January 23, 1971, at Prospect Creek, Alaska, a camp along the Alaskan pipeline in the Endicott Mountains. For comparison, the table on page 78 shows official record low temperatures for the Canadian provinces and territories. Interestingly, in the Arctic Islands, the lowest temperature ever reported was −69.2°F (−56.2°C) at a special International Geophysical Year observing station at Lake Hazen on January 4, 1958.

Unofficially, however, temperatures lower than −81°F (−62.8°C) have been reported. On January 7, 1902, two temporary sites near Fort Nelson, in northeastern British Columbia, reported temperatures of −96°F (−71.1°C) and −92°F (−68.9°C), in connection with a permafrost study, while the temperature at Fort Nelson airport weather station was −43.6°F (−42°C). The extreme temperatures were attributed to intense cold air ponding in mountain valleys during a long, cold, clear night. Though not official, such values indicate that in the right topographic, vegetation and atmospheric conditions, temperatures lower than the official records can, and probably do, occur more often than might generally be supposed.

How about the rest of the world? Snag still compares well: extremes below −80°F (−62.2°C) have occurred in only three other places: northeastern Siberia, central Greenland and Antarctica.

The lowest temperature ever recorded at a weather station—−128.6°F (−89.2°C)—was in eastern Antarctica at the Russian scientific station of Vostok on July 21, 1983. Vostok also held the previous world record, −126.4°F (−88°C) on August 24, 1960. This station, which is not staffed year-round, owes its terrible cold to its lofty height of 3,414 metres above sea level.

Where is the lowest temperature where people live year-round? For many years, the coldest settlement was centred a degree of latitude north

Our most memorable day was the day we watched the DC3 land with new supplies, vegetables, meat, fruit and of course a few cases of beer and liquor. We certainly played some high-stakes poker that night! We had lots of interviews and pictures taken that day. The next day we had some pretty severe hangovers."—Wilf Blezard, Weather Observer at Snag, Yukon

Top Canadian Cold Spots

Province/Territory	°C	Date	Location
Alberta	−61.1	Jan. 11, 1911	Fort Vermilion
British Columbia	−58.9	Jan. 31, 1947	Smith River
Manitoba	−52.8	Jan. 9, 1899	Norway House
New Brunswick	−47.2	Feb. 1, 1955	Sisson Dam
Newfoundland/Labrador	−51.1	Feb. 17, 1973	Esker 2
Northwest Territories	−57.8	Feb. 13, 1973	Shepherd Bay
Nova Scotia	−41.1	Jan. 31, 1920	Upper Stewiacke
Ontario	−58.3	Jan. 23, 1935	Iroquois Falls
Prince Edward Island	−37.2	Jan. 26, 1884	Kilmahumaig
Quebec	−54.4	Feb. 5, 1923	Doucet
Saskatchewan	−56.7	Feb. 1, 1893	Prince Albert
Yukon	−63.0	Feb. 3, 1947	Snag

of the Arctic circle at Verkhoyansk in northern Siberia. It held the world record for low temperatures at −90.4°F (−68°C), registered twice in February 1892. However, some controversy exists about the reliability of the thermometer from which the reading was taken, and there have been several unconfirmed reports of lower temperature recorded elsewhere. Believed to be an even colder place is Oymakon, a village of about 600 people in a mountain valley 700 metres above sea level on the banks of the Indigirka River in northeastern Yakutia. No observations were made in the winter of 1892 at Oymakon, but in later years, it was consistently colder than Verkhoyansk. Oymakon's lowest recorded temperature is −90.4°F (−68°C) in January 1959.

The only other place in the world where temperatures have been colder than −81°F (−62.8°C) is Greenland. On the permanent ice cap in central Greenland, the lowest official temperature for the Western Hemisphere was recorded on January 9, 1954; −86.8°F (−66°C) at Northice (2,341 metres above sea level), a station established by the British North Greenland Expedition. Since Northice was open for only 20 months, it is probable that lower temperatures might be expected there over a longer period of time.

Will Snag remain North America's cold spot? Only time will tell. But one thing is certain: weather observers will no longer have to mark thermometer sheaths when temperatures fall below −80°F. Now, all official alcohol thermometers in Canada have markings to −94°F (−70°C), a thermometer redesign due to the coldest day in Canadian history.

RED RIVER'S FLOOD
OF THE CENTURY

Those living in the Red River valley know the hazards of spring flooding; but not since 1852 have they had to confront the volume of water that flooded the valley in spring 1997. Almost 2,000 square kilometres of valley lands were flooded as the Red River rose 12 metres above winter levels. By the time the river's crest reached downtown Winnipeg on May 2, some 28,000 Manitoba residents had been forced to flee their homes. Unofficial estimates of total damage to public and private property, including infrastructure replacement and flood-proofing, may reach close to $500 million. Thousands of volunteers and soldiers and a brigade of earthmovers worked around the clock in a frantic effort to shore up defenses against the rising waters. Incredibly, damages prevented by flood control works and emergency diking and sandbagging by a flood-weary citizenry have been estimated at more than $6 billion.

What caused the flood? Floods in the Red River watershed have always been associated with ice jams, snowmelt run-off, soggy soils from heavy fall or spring rains, heavy winter snows and, more often, a combination of two or more of these causes.

At the time of freeze-up in 1996, soil moisture by volume was generally 60 to 90 percent of capacity. Freeze-up came quickly. The winter was unusually long and cold with snow cover developing in early November 1996 and remaining until mid-April 1997. On February 25, 1997, Winnipeg's temperature finally rose above freezing for the first time in 108 days—almost four straight months—setting a new record for duration. With a deep snowpack of record amounts, Manitobans were warned in late February that they could be facing the worst flood of the century.

In early April, a nasty snowstorm, the worst in Manitoba history, dumped half a winter's snowfall load in the Red River basin in one weekend. Residents suspended sandbagging for snow shovelling and the capital was shut down for 48 hours. The trajectory of the storm and zone of heavy precipitation included the entire Red River watershed from the northeast tip of South Dakota to Lake Winnipeg. An important feature of the storm was the significant amount of rain it produced in the headwaters area, where the spring run-off had already begun.

In Manitoba, the April snowstorm of 1997 surpassed previous records for most precipitation in a 24-hour period and set new records for the worst April disturbance since Environment Canada began keeping records in 1876.

Following the storm, the temperature in Winnipeg plunged to a new all-time low of –21.6°C, crushing the previous record of –18.9°C set in 1877. No appreciable melting took place for two weeks following the storm, guaranteeing major spring flooding problems. Total basin precipitation from the start of winter to early May was 221 millimetres, about 70 percent above normal.

On April 21, the flood arrived in Manitoba at Emerson, forcing thousands to flee the Red River valley. Rural Manitoba south of Winnipeg was deserted. The entire town of Ste. Agathe, population 500, was submerged. Many rural homes and farms unprotected by dikes were immersed up to their eaves in muddy brown water. Before they were forced out, farmers parked their combines, tractors, farm trucks, seeders, grain bins—even rows of hay bales—on the highest points of land.

The murky waters spread out in all directions. At its peak, the "Red River Sea" stretched as far as the eye could see. Normally 180 kilometres wide, the river in flood spread to some 30 kilometres wide. With winds gusting to 60 kilometres per hour, whitecapped waves pounded sandbag dikes, breaking some and vaulting others. The water was not as deep as it might have been only because the waters spread more widely than expected.

Hydrologists with Manitoba Natural Resources estimated that the 1997 Red River flood was the third largest discharge on the river in about two centuries. The run-off could have been considerably greater had it not been for the snowpack losses prior to the April blizzard and several weeks of dry weather following the blizzard. A wetter than normal spring might have led to the greatest and costliest flood in two centuries. As it was, the great flood of 1997 was the worst in a century and a half.

A church in downtown Ste. Agathe, Manitoba, surrounded by floodwaters. *Tom Hanson/Canapress*

Top Ten Peak Discharges of the Red River in Downtown Winnipeg

(Computed natural flows without existing flood control works)

Year	Estimated Maximum Discharge (cubic metres per second)
1826	6,371
1852	4,672
1997	4,587
1861	3,540
1950	3,058
1996	3,058
1979	3,030
1974	2,718
1966	2,497
1916	2,427

Source: Adapted from A.A. Warkentin

CANADA'S WORST ICE STORM ON RECORD

Ice storms are often winter's worst hazard. More slippery than snow, freezing rain or glaze is tenacious, clinging to every object it touches. A little can be dangerous, a lot can be catastrophic.

These storms are a major hazard in all parts of Canada except the North, but are especially common from Ontario to Newfoundland. The severity of ice storms depends largely on the accumulation of ice, the duration of the event, and the location and extent of the area affected. Based on these criteria, Ice Storm '98 was the worst to hit Canada in recent memory. From January 5 to 10, 1998, the total water equivalent of precipitation, comprising mostly freezing rain and ice pellets plus a bit of snow, exceeded 85 millimetres in Ottawa, 73 in Kingston, 108 in Cornwall and 100 in Montreal. Previous major ice storms in the region, notably December 1986 in Ottawa and February 1961 in Montreal, deposited between 30 and 40 millimetres of ice—about half the thickness from the 1998 storm event!

The extent of the area affected by the ice was enormous. Freezing precipitation is often described in weather reports as "a line of" or "spotty occurrences of." At the peak of the storm, the area of freezing precipitation extended from Muskoka and Kitchener in Ontario through eastern Ontario, western Quebec and the Eastern Townships to the Bay of Fundy coasts of New Brunswick and Nova Scotia. In the United States, icing coated northern New York state and parts of New England.

What made the ice storm so unusual, though, was its duration. On average, Ottawa and Montreal receive freezing precipitation 12 to 17 days a year. Each episode generally lasts for only a few hours at a time, for an annual average total of between 45 to 65 hours. During Ice Storm '98, it did not rain continuously; however, freezing rain and drizzle fell for more than 80 hours—again nearly double the normal annual total.

The storm brutalized one of the largest urban areas of North America, leaving more than 4 million people freezing in the dark for hours, if not days. Without question, the storm directly affected more people than any previous weather event in Canadian history. In the third week following the onset of the storm, more than 700,000 people were still without electricity. Had the storm tracked 100 kilometres farther east or west, the disruptive effect would have been far less crippling.

The damage in eastern Ontario and southern Quebec was so severe that major rebuilding, not repairing, of the electrical grid had to be undertaken. What it took human beings a half century to construct took nature a matter of hours to knock down.

Farmers were especially hard hit. Dairy and hog farmers were left without power, frantically sharing generators to run milking machines and to care for newborn piglets. Many Quebec maple syrup producers, whose trees account for 70 percent of the world supply, were ruined with much of their sugar bush permanently destroyed.

Setting the Scene

For several days prior to the ice storm, a low-pressure weather system over the Texas Panhandle pumped moist, warm air from the Gulf of Mexico into southern Ontario and Quebec at cloud level. At the same time, over Hudson Bay, a large stationary Arctic high pressure area maintained a northeasterly circulation over central Quebec, draining very cold air into the St. Lawrence and Ottawa river valleys. Unable to dislodge the heavy, cold air in the river valleys, the southerly current overrode the wedge of cold air at the surface, setting the scene for the onset of freezing rain.

The weather remained unchanged throughout the week, because out in the Atlantic near Bermuda, a large high-pressure system blocked the Gulf storms from following their normal track across the Atlantic and northward to Iceland. Instead, like a boulder in a stream, the high-pressure system diverted the bulk of the moisture farther west along the western flank of the Appalachian Mountains and into Ontario and Quebec where it collided with the cold Arctic air.

Streams of wet, mild air pushed northward throughout the week. Heavy rains caused deadly flooding in some American states and brought a wet January thaw for much of southwestern Ontario before heading into eastern Ontario. Late on January 9, the main weather system broke down, and surface winds veered southwesterly.

El Niño had a part to play in the ice storm. Since early December, a strong subtropical jet stream had flowed from the Pacific Ocean across the southern United States. This flow typically happens during the mature phase of El Niño and results in increased storminess along the Gulf coast of the United States.

Forecasting a Freezing Rain Storm

Forecasting the occurrence and amount of freezing rain is tricky. While the temperature hovers around the freezing mark, the weather often cannot make up its mind whether to drop liquid or frozen precipitation or some congealed mixture. A one-degree temperature swing on either side of freezing can make all the difference in the type of precipitation that falls.

For freezing precipitation, the atmosphere must be properly layered—a layer of warm air aloft with temperatures above freezing, sandwiched between layers of colder air with temperatures below freezing. Often in winter the warm, moist air overrides the heavier, denser cold air near the surface.

When rain falls, or snow melts while falling through the intermediary warm layer, rain falls into the shallow cold layer hugging the ground. There, with the air temperature below freezing and/or the ground and objects still below freezing, the chilled raindrops freeze but not completely. Instead, they reach the surface as a supercooled liquid (water droplets at a temperature below 0°C) or as a mixture of liquid and ice. Upon striking a colder object, such as the pavement, hydro wires, tree branches, building walls or cars, the supercooled raindrops spread out and freeze almost immediately, forming a smooth, thin veneer of slick ice. Freezing rain or glaze contains no air bubbles and looks as smooth and clear as glass. If the drops are tiny (less than 0.5 millimetres in diameter), the precipitation is called freezing drizzle.

Road skating in Montreal at the height of the January 1998 ice storm. *Alain Roberge/Canapress*

How the Storm Affected Eastern Canada

- At least 25 deaths, many from hypothermia and carbon-monoxyde poisoning.
- About 900,000 households without power in Quebec; 100,000 in Ontario.
- Residents were urged to boil water for 24 to 48 hours.
- Airlines and railways discouraged travel into the area.
- Sixteen thousand troops (including 2,300 reservists) were deployed to help with clean-up, evacuation and security.
- Millions of residents were forced into mobile living, visiting family to shower and share a meal, moving in temporarily with friends or staying at a shelter.
- Prolonged freezing rain brought down millions of trees, 120,000 kilometres of power lines and telephone cables, 130 major transmission towers (each worth $100,000) and about 30,000 wooden utility poles costing $3,000 each.

Weather Across Canada

An ice field formed on a Calgary street following a massive hailstorm in July 1996.
Jim Wells/Canapress

FOREST BLOWDOWN—
A BLOW-BY-BLOW
ACCOUNT

On November 6, 1994, savage winds of over 100 kilometres per hour buffeted parts of eastern Canada. In Ontario and Quebec, the storm blew down road signs, uprooted trees and downed power lines, leaving thousands of Ottawa-area customers without electricity. It was a major squall, but hardly unusual for the windiest month of the year.

By the time the raging storm whipped through New Brunswick the next day, however, its power was the stuff of myths. What turned out to be one of the most widespread, catastrophic windstorms in a quarter of a century had felled 15 million trees, among them hectare upon hectare of mature balsam fir and spruce.

A ferocious windstorm can ravage a forest, brutally stripping trees of their needles and leaves, snapping massive trunks and uprooting and toppling entire stands, just as this one did. In the end, three million cubic metres of wood—nearly half the allowable annual cut of softwood in the province—lay on the forest floor. From the air, the area south of Mount Carleton Provincial Park resembled nothing less than a giant game of pickup sticks.

Foresters have names for these winds that blow with such devastation. Windthrow or blowdown occurs when soil rootballs can't resist the wind pressure and trees are literally lifted out of the earth with their massive balls of tangled soil and roots intact. Windbreak or windsnap, which occurs less commonly, fractures treetops and snaps trunks at ground level or above. It happens when wind stress isn't enough to dislodge the roots, but still causes wood fibre to break or buckle. As the stress increases, more fibre breaks and trunks or branches snap as a result.

During an average windstorm, individual trees are struck by as many as 2,000 strong gusts. The continual bombardment weakens the whole system by breaking fibres in the stem, snapping fine roots and disrupting the contact between the roots and the soil.

Barry Gardiner, a forest researcher with the Forestry Authority in the United Kingdom, has experienced forest blowdown first-hand: "Trees start swaying around but not particularly far, and then a gust comes along which pushes them too far and they go right to the ground. The ground heaves so much that you become quite disoriented, like being in an earthquake." Gardiner compares the effect of a gust's force on a tree to a straight left jab to the jaw. "There's a sudden impact, [and] the tree rocks back and forth. [It] returns to an upright position just in time for the next blow." The knockdown punch comes when a second gust batters a tree while it is still in the grip of the first. The added drag on the tree increases the amplitude of the sway beyond a critical breaking point.

Forest blowdown occurs in Canada more frequently than most people realize. Winds capable of blowing down trees can occur at any time of the year because they accompany weather systems that are quite common in most regions. Some of the culprits:

- *Cyclonic storms.* These weather systems, which include hurricanes, can cause spectacular damage, as did the one that hit New Brunswick in November 1994. But even that storm paled by comparison with the cyclone that struck British Columbia and the American Pacific Northwest in October 1962. In the aftermath, coastal forests, exposed to gusts exceeding 155 km/h, suffered huge losses. About 30 million cubic metres of timber were downed, much of it not salvageable for lumber.

The windstorm that felled all those trees in New Brunswick on November 6, 1994, also forced the cancellation of the final six horse races at Toronto's Woodbine track. Jockeys voted unanimously to stop riding after four races. "I've never felt gusts like that," jockey Sandy Hawley said. "When I went out for the post parade before the fourth race, my helmet would have blown away, had it not been for my chin strap. The winds were tolerable in the first race, but I knew if they got worse that there would be problems. Horses were being blown sideways in the post parade."

- *Tornadoes.* Estimates suggest about one tornado strikes annually for every 10,000 square kilometres of forests in Ontario and Quebec. From the air, you can easily see the damage a tornado causes. Its path is fairly narrow (from a few metres to a kilometre), there's frequent skipping and the landscape is strewn haphazardly with twisted, snapped and uprooted trees.

- *Thunderstorms.* We're not talking about your garden-variety storm here, but rather about an organized system of severe thunderstorms made up of powerful updrafts and downdrafts. They range in scale from microbursts covering less than 4 kilometres and lasting just 10 minutes, to violent downbursts that can span 400 kilometres and last for an hour or more. Downbursts commonly occur when a low-pressure system combines with thunderstorms. Cold dense air plummets rapidly from the top of the thunderstorm and spreads horizontally along the ground. If an upper-level jet stream strengthens the downdraft and joins with the general movement of the storm, winds at the ground may reach 250 kilometres per hour, with potentially devastating results. Case in point: on July 17, 1991, north of Kenora, Ontario, a family of downbursts flattened 30 million trees over 1,500 square kilometres. In 15 minutes, the windstorm levelled six years' worth of timber harvest—the largest blowdown in the province's history. On some roads, trees were piled as high as a two-storey building.

A single, strong blast lasting a few seconds, rather than a steady wind, causes most destruction. Here's why: as the air flows over a varied landscape of trees, buildings and hills, surface friction breaks the wind into a series of irregular lulls and gusts, which can have twice the speed of a steady wind. The rougher the landscape and the stronger the sustained wind, the more prone the air is to gusting. Forest surfaces are particularly rough: the wind over them is much more turbulent than over pavement or farmland. The more complex the terrain, the more the wind speeds up, especially through narrowing valleys and over high ridges. Forest blowdown is often worse, for example, on the sheltered lee slopes of mountains, where turbulence with particularly increased wind

Cleaning up after a forest blowdown. *Judy Gallant/Repap*

speed can develop.

Whether a tree snaps off, blows down or stays put depends on more than wind velocity, however. Several factors either increase the pressure or the stress on a tree or reduce its resistance to wind.

The species of tree makes a difference. Deciduous trees, for example, are usually more windfirm than evergreens. For one thing, because they're usually leafless during the windiest time of the year, they intercept less wind.

Size is another factor. Tall trees are more vulnerable, particularly when taller means older. Older trees suffer a higher incidence of injury, insect infestation, root and butt rot and other diseases that predispose them to wind damage.

Shape also determines the amount of stress that wind exerts on a tree's stem and root. Tall, slender, cylindrical trunks, such as balsam fir, sway more than short, conical trunks of, say, black spruce or hemlock. Uprooted trees tend to be larger, with denser, stiffer and stronger wood than trees snapped in the wind.

When the Mount St. Helens volcano erupted in 1980, every tree within 24 kilometres of the crater was toppled by the wind from the volcanic blast.

Harvesting, thinning and cutting also affect a forest's ability to withstand a storm: changes to a forest's structure can cause more turbulence and accelerate the wind. That's why heavier damage to trees usually occurs near gaps in the stand, by roadsides and rail lines, in burned areas and along lakes and rivers. A tree's first line of defence against wind is canopy density. Wherever openings permit winds to dip down into the canopy, trees are more susceptible to blowdown.

Heavy accumulations of snow break down branches and even whole trees, or, in other cases, produce permanent bends in their trunks. The greatest sufferers from "snow-break" injury are the evergreens. Their dense masses of needles offer a firm lodging for the snow. Ice formed from falling rain causes much more widespread damage to trees than does snow.

Trees are better protected if they have strongly interlocked soil and roots. Anything that reduces the strength or adhesion quality of the soil—erosion, acid rain, road salt, soil compaction or breaks in roots—can put a tree at greater risk. Even a weak storm can break fine roots and disrupt the contact between roots and the soil.

The texture of the soil often helps determine the kind of damage trees will sustain from wind. Trees rooted in shallow rocky terrain or poorly drained soil are more vulnerable to windthrow, whereas those in frozen or compacted dry soil tend to break off at the trunk before uprooting. If the ground had been frozen when the storm struck New Brunswick in 1994, for example, fewer trees would have been blown down.

But it wasn't. In New Brunswick in the summer of 1995, workers mounted an enormous salvaging operation to harvest whatever they could of the fallen wood. Much of the year's logging plans were scrapped so that loggers and machinery could be mobilized for a massive clean-up in the blowdown area. The work was critical. Downed trees are an ideal breeding ground for insects and fungus; the resulting disease and rot reduce valuable logs to pulp in less than two years and can spread to standing trees. There's also an increased risk of forest fires: fallen trees become kindling waiting to ignite. During a fire, downed trees slow firefighters and make fire control practically impossible. The havoc an ill wind can cause lasts long after a storm stills.

WEATHERING HEIGHTS—
A GLOBAL WARNING?

An increasing number of climatologists believe that unusual and record-breaking weather events are becoming more common and may even be the "fingerprints" of global warming.

On average, the world is 0.5°C warmer today than it was a century ago, with more than half of the increase coming in the past 20 years. Globally, 11 of the 12 warmest years on record have occurred since 1980, with 1997 being the warmest. A warmer-than-normal year is not necessarily proof of climate change; for perspective, longer-term trends worldwide from a decade or more must be assessed. In December 1995, an international panel of scientists did just that and concluded that "global mean temperature changes over the last century are unlikely to be entirely due to natural causes ... Evidence suggests a discernible human influence on global climate."

The earth's 10 warmest years since 1881 have been: 1981, 1983, 1987, 1988, 1990, 1991, 1994, 1995, 1996 and 1997.

There is more to climate change than higher temperatures though. Computer models of the atmosphere predict that global warming would also bring more volatile weather and related disasters. Climatologists and others who monitor trends and extremes suggest this is already happening. The summer of 1995, for example, began with floods and fires of near-biblical proportions. In June, record rains in Alberta caused once-in-100-year floods on more than a dozen rivers. High waters forced 4,000 people from their homes in Medicine Hat. Flooding may have also contributed to an outbreak of botulism that killed more than 30,000 ducks. Damages topped $50 million. At the same time, dry conditions elsewhere contributed to the second-worst year in Canada's history for forest fires, which consumed some seven million hectares nationwide—an area roughly the size of New Brunswick.

Canada's average temperature increased by 1.1°C between 1895 and 1995.

The year also saw the warmest June and July in the past century. The nation's hot spot was Thunder Bay, Ontario, where the mercury rose to an all-time high of 39°C on June 18. Ontario and Quebec experienced what may have been the most humid summer, with the humidex in Windsor, Ontario, soaring to 50°C on July 14—the highest ever reported in Canada. In Toronto, nighttime temperatures stayed above the 20°C mark 33 times. In all, there were 26 very humid days, compared with the average 15. To keep its customers cool, Ontario Hydro produced electricity at an all-time summer record level. Remarkably, no human deaths were directly attributed to the heat. But on one particulary steamy August weekend, a half million chickens and turkeys died of heat stroke.

The globally average surface temperature of the earth is 15°C; without the greenhouse effect it would be a chilly -18°C.

The heat and humidity fuelled some of the most destructive storms ever seen in parts of the country. In central and southern Ontario, winds reached 150 to 200 kilometres per hour on July 15, contributing to property losses of $20 million. In Saskatchewan, hailstorms or tornadoes were observed for 10 consecutive days during June. But it was a plough wind that damaged every property and stripped trees bare in Oxbow and Pilot Butte. Calgary and Edmonton lived up to their reputation as major hailstorm cities. In the first 18 days of July, Calgary had 11 thunderstorms, 4 dropping ice balls. And in Edmonton, road crews twice had to use snowploughs to remove hail from city streets.

The world is clearly warmer today than it was a century ago. The earth has warmed by about 0.5°C between 1861 and 1995, with most of the increase coming in the past 30 years. Of significance, nighttime temperatures are rising three times faster than daytime temperatures.

But perhaps most remarkable were the nine tropical storms, including six hurricanes, that swept into Canada in 1995. The norm is one a year. And on September 11, a 30-metre wave struck the *QE2* cruise ship south of Nova Scotia—the highest wave ever recorded in the world.

Pumpkins had barely been carved and rakes put away when brittle cold and unending snows arrived over many parts of North America. Parts of central Ontario received a year's worth of snow before the first official day of winter, with Ottawa and Montreal digging out from the snowiest and coldest November and December on record. In western Canada, the January 1996 thaw arrived right on schedule, but was followed closely by a record-breaking cold spell with temperatures plunging to a low of −52°C. Given three straight weeks of frigid weather, most westerners were wishing for even a breath of global warmth. For most Canadians, the only comfort was being part of a historic cold spell. Climatologists were left explaining to an incredulous public that there was actually a link between record cold, paralyzing blizzards and global warming.

Industrialized countries produce 74 percent of the CO_2 going into the atmosphere in 1985, developing countries about 24 percent. Canada consumes about 2.6 percent of world's energy, but only represents 0.56 percent of the world total population.

The story was much the same around the world in 1995–96. More than 800 people died during a heat wave that gripped the midwestern United States; upward of 550 died in Chicago alone, where the temperature soared to 40°C on July 13. Britons witnessed the third-hottest spell since 1659, and the driest in 200 years. From Spain to Greece, searing heat was blamed for dozens of deaths and brushfires. In western Russia and Ukraine, maximum temperatures soared to 47°C. Heavy rains continued to soak parts of central and northeast China, while dryness prevailed elsewhere. Record floods in the southern Yangtze River Valley killed 450 people and stranded three million others.

If all of Greenland's icecap melted, sea levels would rise by 7.5 metres; if the Antarctic icecap melted, global sea levels would rise by 65 metres.

It would be fiction to interpret every weather catastrophe, every few weeks with heat and rain or every "storm of the century" as clear evidence that the earth is warming up. Just as any heat wave does not prove the theory of global warming, any lengthy cold snap doesn't mean the threat of the greenhouse effect is a lot of "hot air." The earth-atmosphere system is complex and variable.

The frozen continent of Antarctica has warmed a whopping 2.5°C in the past 50 years. In the 1970s, glaciologists predicted melting of the Antarctic ice shelf would be a clear signal of global warming. In 1995, an enormous chunk of ice, 37 by 77 kilometres in size, broke loose from the western Antarctic ice shelf and floated out to sea. The 200-metre-thick iceberg was the size of Prince Edward Island.

Although it's tempting to connect weather surprises with humankind's increased burning of fossil fuels, weather extremes and "yo-yo" temperature swings may have nothing to do with global warming. Instead, they may only be random meteorological aberrations—all part of the natural year-to-year variations in weather. Recent freakish weather is just as likely to be blamed on curvier jet streams, more frequent and longer El Niños or changes in sunspots.

Most scientists do agree that small changes in temperature trends will lead to larger changes in the frequency of extreme and unusual weather. Their understanding comes largely from the performance of highly sophisticated computer models. Much of what we have observed in temperature trends in the past 100 years is consistent with model projections of the combined effects of greenhouse gases and aerosols on world climates. The global models were impressive in demonstrating the cooling trend following the eruption of Mount Pinatubo in the Philippines and the warm atmosphere resurgence after the volcano's effect had abated.

However, climate models can as yet only give us some very broad indications of how weather extremes may change. For instance, they suggest that:

- Even a small warming could lead to large increases in the frequency and intensity of droughts, floods and forest fires
- Hurricanes in a greenhouse-warmed world may be generally weaker, but once formed, they have the potential to stay intact longer as they move farther north
- Weather would likely bring more destructive tornadoes, severe hailstorms, intense thunderstorms and windstorms

Over the past decade or so, observational evidence suggests that the world's weather is not just warming up, but it's also becoming more volatile and variable. For example, recent studies reveal that:

- Between 1991 and 1994, there were three El Niños in 4 years—unprecedented in the past 200 years. In recent years, these warming episodes have been more frequent and more intense, including two "El Niños of the century" separated by only 15 years

- In the past 10 years, the American Southeast has experienced its worst drought in 300 years, and the Midwest has had its worst flood in history

- Since 1980, Canada has suffered five of the worst forest-fire years in history

- The worst bush fires in 200 years ravaged eastern Australia at the close of 1993

- Insurance claims due to natural disasters in the 1980s were tenfold greater than in the 1960s and even higher in 1991 and 1992; storms have accounted for 88 percent of the disasters in the past decade; also in the past decade, 10 of Canada's costliest natural disasters have involved severe storms

The difference in global temperature between now and the last ice age is only 4.5°C.

- Worldwide catastrophic windstorms numbered 29 during the 1980s, 14 in the 1970s and 8 in the 1960s. In 1992–93 alone, hurricanes, floods and blizzards in the United States inflicted more than $65 billion in property damages and losses to its economy

It is too soon to link definitively all this wild and extreme weather to global warming. But when many unusual weather events happen at the same time—and year after year—it is hard to attribute them all to natural variability. "Increasingly, the gut feeling is that they are linked to global warming," says Henry Hengeveld, science adviser on climate change for Environment Canada.

The worst and best Canadian weather

We often hear gibes about our weather from foreigners and fellow Canadians alike. In certain parts of Canada, climate presents many hardships. Icebergs crowding into the bays and inlets of Newfoundland prevent fishers from leaving harbours and threaten their boats and fish-

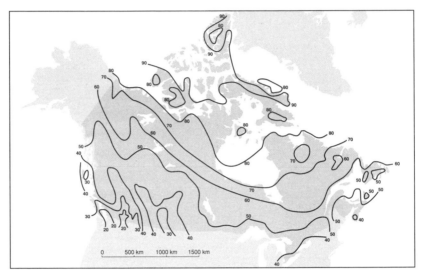

Climate severity index (maximum 100 points).

ing gear. Each year residents of southern Ontario normally endure steamy heat and humidity in summer and blinding whiteouts and bitter cold in winter, even if only infrequently or for short periods of time. Weeks of fog and drizzle depress coastal British Columbians, and Arctic inhabitants feel fortunate when it doesn't snow in July.

Although the Canadian climate is mostly pleasant—though also stimulating, invigorating and challenging—its unfavourable aspects do create hardship. What are the climatic stresses and ameliorants, where is the perfect "10" climate, who has the best and worst weather in Canada, and, from a climate point of view, where are the most depressing, hazardous, uncomfortable and confining places in Canada?

Knowledge of climate severity can be valuable to employers concerned about the timing of outdoor activities and workers' performance; to workers seeking fair and equitable remuneration for working outdoors or in isolated areas; for planners or designers of workplaces, residences, recreational areas, clothing and equipment; and to persons who are retiring, or seeking havens from certain climate-related illnesses. For this reason, Environment Canada devised the climate severity index (CSI). It rates a locale's climate in terms of human comfort and well-being. The index has a range from 1 to 100 with a score of 1 representing the least severe climate and 100 the most.

The CSI quantifies the unfavourable aspects of the Canadian climate by weighting 17 year-round climate stresses that are generally considered to be extreme or severe. Some stresses include extremes of hot or cold, wetness or dryness, and windiness; continuous darkness or daylight; prolonged or intense precipitation, fog, restricted visibility; lightning and severe weather like thunderstorms, blowing snow and freezing precipitation.

A Newcomer's Guide to Canada **was revised by the Canadian government in 1995 after experts determined it was riddled with errors and bad advice. Among the mistakes:**

▪ Canadian weather was very warm in summer

▪ Newcomers learn to enjoy winter

CSIs for Major Canadian Cities*

City	CSI	City	CSI
Victoria, BC	13	Halifax, NS	43
Vancouver, BC	18	Montreal, PQ	44
Calgary, AB	34	Sudbury, ON	46
Toronto, ON	35	Regina, SK	47
Hamilton, ON	35	Charlottetown, PEI	48
Edmonton, AB	37	Saint John, NB	48
Windsor, ON	37	Winnipeg, MB	51
London, ON	41	Québec, PQ	52
Saskatoon, SK	42	Chicoutimi-Jonquière, PQ	54
Ottawa, ON	43	St. John's, NF	56

* These values are estimates for central city locations. In some cases, there are differences between these and the values estimated for airport sites.

Since most relationships between climate and psychophysiological sensations are not well understood, one must rely principally on personal experience and observation in deciding what elements to include and their relative importance.

To devise the CSI, advice about stressful climate situations was sought from employees in the Canadian weather service at Downsview, Ontario, many of whom have worked several years in at least two remote Canadian locations. They were asked to list, in order, those aspects of climate considered most stressful (unfavourable) in the places where they had worked. The wide variety of responses was not unexpected, considering the number and diversity of work settings. Prominent among the weather excesses were cold, wind, darkness and continuous precipitation.

The index takes into account the four major factors most directly related to environmental stress: winter and summer discomfort; psychological state; hazardousness or safety of a place; and limitations on mobility of travel. Considering the importance of comfort in our daily lives, which influences what we wear, how we feel, if and how we travel and how effectively we work and play, this factor was considered the most important in the CSI. Psychological state and hazardousness are complementary factors but were judged to be of lesser importance than comfort because they are generally associated with less frequent and more ephemeral factors. Although weather restricts outdoor mobility, especially in winter, it is less significant as a year-round disruptive element than the three others.

Avon tested its revolutionary new lipstick, Beyond Color, on the lips of 20 women in Winnipeg. In choosing Winnipeg, the company settled on the city with the coldest winters of any major city in the world. Its average January low temperature is –23.6°C. Winnipeg is also Canada's sunniest city during the winter, presenting another serious threat to lips and skin. The product is reputed to be a four-season success, proven to protect against scorching heat and dryness as well.

Percentage Weightings Assigned to the Factors and Sub-factors Composing the Climate Severity Index

DISCOMFORT (50 POINTS)

Winter Discomfort (35 Points)

1. *Wind Chill*
   Mean percentage of time in January that wind chill exceeds 1,400 W/m^2 — 15
2. *Length of Winter*
   Number of months with a mean daily temperature of less than 0°C — 10
3. *Severity of Winter*
   Mean daily temperature of coldest month — 10

Summer Discomfort (15 Points)

4. *Humidex*
   Mean percentage of days with humidex greater than 30°C for one hour or more — 5
5. *Length of Summer*
   Number of months with a mean daily temperature of 10°C or greater — 2.5
6. *Warmth of Summer*
   Mean daily maximum temperature of warmest month — 2.5
7. *Dampness*
   Mean July wet-bulb depression — 5

PSYCHOLOGICAL STATE (20 POINTS)

8. *Darkness*
   Increasing darkness factor with increasing latitude — 7
9. *Sunshine*
   Mean annual number of hours of bright sunshine — 5
10. *Wet Days*
    Annual number of days with measurable precipitation — 5
11. *Fog*
    Absolute frequency in 10 years of number of days with fog — 3

HAZARDOUSNESS (20 POINTS)

12. *Strong Winds*
    Mean percentage frequency of wind speed equal to
    or greater than 30.6 km/h—average of January and July — 6
13. *Thunderstorms*
    Absolute frequency in 10 years of number of hours with thunder — 2
14. *Blowing Snow*
    Absolute frequency in 10 years of number of hours with blowing snow — 8
15. *Snowfall*
    Mean winter snowfall (cm) — 4

OUTDOOR MOBILITY (10 POINTS)

16. *Visibility*
    Absolute frequency in 10 years on number of hours with a) fog, b) snow, and c) rain — 4
17. *Freezing Precipitation*
    Absolute frequency in 10 years of number of hours with freezing precipitation — 4
18. *Snowfall*
    Mean winter snowfall (cm) — 2

Climate Severity Index for Canadian Airport Locations

British Columbia
Abbotsford 21
Cape St. James 41
Castlegar 29
Comox 22
Cranbrook 24
Dease Lake 44
Fort Nelson 47
Fort St. John 44
Hope 28
Kamloops 20
Penticton 16
Port Hardy 30
Prince George 38
Prince Rupert 34
Quesnel 32
Sandspit 30
Smithers 35
Terrace 46
Tofino 28
Vancouver 19
Victoria 15
Williams Lake 26

Yukon
Dawson 54
Watson Lake 52
Whitehorse 46

Northwest Territories
Alert 84
Baker Lake 79
Cambridge Bay 82
Cape Dyer 88
Clyde 74
Coppermine 73
Coral Harbour 78
Ennadai Lake 77
Eureka 75
Fort Simpson 53
Fort Smith 52
Hall Beach 86
Hay River 50
Inuvik 63
Iqaluit 76
Mould Bay 93
Norman Wells 61
Resolute 95
Sachs Harbour 78
Yellowknife 57

Alberta
Calgary 35
Cold Lake 42
Coronation 37

Edmonton (minicipal) 37
Edmonton International 43
Edson 38
Embarras 46
Fort Chipewyan 49
Fort McMurray 46
Fort Vermilion 42
Grande Prairie 40
High Level 46
Lethbridge 33
Medicine Hat 29
Peace River 42
Red Deer 41
Rocky Mountain House 35
Slave Lake 46
Vermilion 39
Whitecourt 39

Saskatchewan
Cree Lake 51
Estevan 45
Meadow Lake 39
Moose Jaw 45
North Battleford 40
Prince Albert 46
Regina 49
Saskatoon 42
Yorkton 48

Manitoba
Brochet 57
Churchill 82
Dauphin 49
Flin Flon 49
Gimli 52
Portage La Prairie 49
Rivers 49
The Pas 52
Thompson 53
Winnipeg 51

Ontario
Atikokan 50
Gore Bay 43
Kenora 50
London 41
Moosonee 56
Mount Forest 49
Muskoka 43
North Bay 46
Ottawa 44
Sault Ste. Marie 46
Simcoe 39
Sudbury 54
Thunder Bay 44

Timmins 53
Toronto 36
Trenton 39
Trout Lake 60
White River 48
Wiarton 45
Windsor 37

Quebec
Chapais 64
Chicoutimi-Jonquière 56
Fort Chimo 64
Grindstone Island 48
Inukjuak 77
Mont-Joli 55
Montreal 43
Nitchequon 67
Poste-de-la-Baleine 70
Quebec 52
Rivière-au-Renard 53
St-Hubert 45
Schefferville 71
Sept-Iles 57
Sherbrooke 43
Val-d'Or 54

New Brunswick
Campbellton 41
Charlo 49
Chatham 43
Fredericton 41
Moncton 47
Saint John 48

Nova Scotia
Greenwood 42
Halifax 47
Sable Island 44
Shearwater 42
Sydney 50
Truro 42
Yarmouth 40

Prince Edward Island
Charlottetown 48
Summerside 49

Newfoundland
Argentia 46
Daniels Harbour 55
Gander 58
Goose 58
Hopedale 70
St. John's 59
Stephenville 47

Discomfort

Winter is the most stressful time of the year in Canada. According to Statistics Canada, an average of almost 110 persons die each year from exposure to extreme cold temperatures, whereas 17 die from all other natural events, such as lightning, storms, floods, heat waves, earthquakes and tidal waves. The largest temperature contrasts occur during winter in Canada, while little contrast occurs during summer south of the Arctic Circle.

Three elements were used to define the winter discomfort factor: the degree of coldness (wind chill), the duration of winter and its severity. Wind chill is a recognized index of heat loss and cold injury for humans, combining the effects of low temperature and strong winds. The duration or length of winter is determined by calculating the number of months with a mean daily temperature of less than 0°C, and the severity of winter, by the mean daily temperature of the coldest month.

Summer discomfort can be defined by four sub-factors: season duration (the number of months with a mean daily temperature of 10°C or more), a measure of the summer's warmth (the mean daily maximum temperature of the warmest month), humidex and dampness. Humidex is now an accepted index of summer discomfort. The mean percentage of days with a humidex value of 30°C for one hour or more at the height of summer was used as an indicator of heat. At a humidex value of

◄ **Even though Canada's climates are diverse and demanding, they are by no means the most extreme that nature can offer. Canada holds none of the world's major weather records. Worse storms and greater extremes of cold, heat, wetness and dryness occur elsewhere.**

◄ **The diversity of the Canadian climate is evident in the number and variety of Canada's climatic landscapes— permanently frozen icecaps, windswept treeless tundra, luxuriant Pacific rain forests, hot semi-arid scrub lands, polar deserts and sun-drenched grainfields. The only climates not found in Canada are the true desert and the equatorial rain forest.**

Canadian Weather Superlatives

Of the 75 largest cities in Canada, each with a population of at least 10,000 and with a nearby weather station, here are the weather champions:

Warmest summers	Kelowna
Warmest place year-round	Vancouver
Coldest winters	Yellowknife
Coldest place year-round	Yellowknife
Snowiest	Sept-Iles
Lowest snowfall	Victoria
Most days below freezing	Thompson
Fewest days below freezing	Vancouver
Longest frost-free period	Vancouver
Shortest frost-free period	Thompson
Wettest	Prince Rupert
Driest	Medicine Hat
Most thunderstorms	London
Fewest thunderstorms	Victoria
Sunniest year-round	Estevan
Sunniest winters	Winnipeg
Sunniest summers	Yellowknife
Most days with blowing snow	Chicoutimi
Most days with freezing rain	St. John's
Foggiest	St. John's
Fog-free	Penticton
Cloudiest skies	Prince Rupert
Clearest skies	Estevan
Most humid	Windsor
Windiest	St. John's

30°C, some people become uncomfortable (below this value almost everyone is comfortable). Dampness can be expressed by the mean wet-bulb depression in July—i.e., the difference between the dry-bulb and wet-bulb temperatures. The smaller this difference, the more "close" or damp the weather.

Psychological State

My colleagues at Environment Canada frequently blamed weather for a host of psychological complaints, including fatigue, depression, irritability, sleep loss, lack of concentration, headaches, general nervousness, forgetfulness, photophobia (light intolerance), chest and joint pain. Weather is also blamed for spells of "cabin fever" or general monotony among personnel in isolated postings.

The climate elements that best represent psychological state and could be readily tabulated from primary weather data were winter day length, annual number of hours of bright sunshine, annual number of days with measurable precipitation and the frequency of hours with fog.

Long periods of darkness, a characteristic of high-latitude winters, are known to be especially detrimental—adversely affecting moods, attitudes and behaviour. Most personnel who have lived for extended periods in the Arctic say the 24 hours of total darkness in winter is particularly debilitating. Some even suggest that the converse in summer, 24 hours of continuous light, is wearing at times. At the latitude of the Arctic Circle, 66.5°N, the polar night does last 24 hours. The length of the polar night increases non-uniformly with latitude, so that at the North Pole, it is six months long.

Sunshine has important physiological and psychological implications. Clear, sunny weather, especially occurring at the end of a long spell of overcast, can be mentally uplifting.

Frequent wet or foggy days can be demoralizing. This is especially true for northern residents, who, after enduring a long winter, feel discouraged if precipitation occurs frequently during the warmest time of the year. This feeling is somewhat similar to that experienced by those who spend the winter months in total darkness.

On February 23, 1996, Canadian meteorologists attending an American Meteorological Society meeting in Atlanta created quite a stir with their campaign, "If you have the instrument ... We've got the weather." They were trying to convince weather-instrument manufacturers that Canada had some of the worst weather in the world and would be an excellent test site for their instruments, especially in Newfoundland. Several companies were eager to try their wares in Canada.

Hazardousness

Elements of climate either singly or together can produce widespread injury and death and bring about considerable damage to property and the environment. Obvious examples are floods and blizzards, which may seriously disrupt entire communities. Extreme wind chill in winter and excessive heat and humidity in summer are also hazardous.

The weather hazardousness of a locale was determined by considering the average winter snowfall and the frequencies of three other elements: strong winds, thunderstorms and blowing snow. These phenomena can cause a host of problems, including possible death, injuries, missed social and business events, delayed services and other privations. Heavy snowfalls create many personal hardships because of confinement and possible shortages of food and fuel. In populated areas, heavy snowfalls are usually accompanied by a spate of heart attacks due to overexertion. Thunderstorms, in particular, are a good indicator of severe weather—hail, windstorms and tornadoes. Blowing and drifting snow create dangerous outdoor travel conditions, stranding people in perilous situations. In fact, all outdoor activity becomes extremely hazardous if near-zero visibilities in blowing snow are combined with high wind chill. Under such conditions, farmers have become lost and died of exposure while attempting to walk from the barn to the house.

Outdoor Mobility

Our ability to move about, to travel to work, school and shopping is restricted by adverse weather. Three sub-factors were identified as restricting outdoor travel and access: total snowfall, freezing precipitation and limited visibility. In Canada, snowfall must be taken into account for assessing the ease of outdoor movement on foot and by vehicle. Freezing precipitation restricts all forms of transportation from walking to flying. In addition, it frequently plays havoc with communication, owing to downed telephone and hydro wires. Visibility reduced by fog, snow or rain also limits our ability to move about and travel.

For 146 airport locations in Canada, points were assigned for 17 weather elements, depending on weather extremes, intensity and duration. For example, a station with long winters (the number of months with a mean daily temperature of less than 0°C lasting 10 or more months) was assigned full points for length of winter, whereas one with no months meeting the criteria was assigned zero points for this sub-factor. The sum of the 17 sub-factors for each of the 4 major factors, weighted by the importance of each factor, yielded the degree of climate severity for that station. The CSI is designed so that values approaching 100 indicate the highest severity.

In Canada, much of the northern Queen Elizabeth Islands, except for some sheltered locations, have the highest severity values, with all four factors showing high values. Only slightly lower severity values were given to the remainder of the Arctic Islands, the Beaufort Sea coast, the district of Keewatin, northern Manitoba, the Hudson Bay coast of Ontario, the Ungava Peninsula and Hudson Strait shores of Quebec and northern Labrador.

Over the remainder of Canada, the severity values are much lower. For example, Medicine Hat (29) and Lethbridge (33) are relatively benign. The table on page 102 lists CSI values for some of Canada's major cities. It shows what residents of Victoria (15) always knew—they have the "best" climate in the country. St. John's (55) wins the prize for the city with the toughest climate. The honour of having the absolute worst climate in Canada (99) goes to a place that no longer exists, Isachsen weather station in the Northwest Territories. Isachsen was closed down in 1978.

FROM TELEGRAPH TO INTERNET—CANADA'S WEATHER SERVICE

As rain began to fall on August 25, 1873, residents of the outports and farms on Cape Breton Island secured their doors and shutters against a rising wind. Few people on this rugged island expected anything more than a late-summer gale. But that night, after gathering strength for a week in the mid-Atlantic, a hurricane spiralled up the coast of the United States and smashed headlong into Cape Breton's east shore.

Almost 90 percent of Canadians listen to weather forecasts daily and find them accurate enough to be useful.

By mid-afternoon the next day, the "Great Nova Scotian Cyclone" had laid waste to a large swath of Cape Breton. Newspapers were filled with accounts of steamers driven aground and bridges washed away in the deluge that accompanied the high winds. The storm's final toll: almost 1,000 people dead, some 1,200 ships sunk or smashed and hundreds of homes destroyed.

Tragically, meteorologists in Toronto knew a day in advance that the hurricane would make landfall in the Maritimes, but no alarm was raised because the telegraph lines to Halifax were down.

Aside from the waterlogged farms and wind-whipped coastal towns of Cape Breton, the hurricane was felt most 1,500 kilometres to the west, in Ottawa. Politicians, prompted by the public outcry over the disaster, voted $37,000 for the development of a national weather warning system. This was a major boost for Canada's fledgling weather service, which had been set up only two years earlier, in 1871, with a sum of $5,000.

The primary mission of a meteorological service is to get the weather word out to the public quickly. No matter how perfect the forecast, if it does not reach the public in time, it has no value. As a result, the Canadian weather service has always been one of the largest consumers of telecommunications services in Canada, creating and adapting tech-

Observing air temperature at a Canadian Arctic weather station. *Environment Canada*

nologies to deliver more weather information to more people more quickly.

In fact, telecommunications helped transform meteorology from an interesting to a practical science, and made national weather services possible. In turn, society's basic need for weather warnings has often been the impetus behind the development of communications devices such as the telegraph, radiotelephone and automatic telephone-answering systems. Telecommunications and weather services have evolved hand in hand.

Meteorology, and forecasting, was still in its formative years in the mid-1800s. If you lived in Canada West or Canada East, you likely divined your own weather forecast based on local conditions and accumulated weather lore—"Red sky at night, sailor's delight," for example.

Samuel Morse's invention of the electric telegraph in 1844 signalled a new age in meteorology. For the first time, forecasters had a tool with which to relay observations over vast distances, to warn towns in the path of a storm—if the lines were not damaged—and to inform others of sunny skies ahead.

By 1876, land lines linked all major cities in eastern Canada. Public weather forecasts were issued from Toronto at 10 a.m. every day except

....➤

Canadians make more than 60 million telephone calls a year to find out the weather forecast.

Sunday and covered the following 24 hours. Compared with today's forecast, they were short and simple. For example, the forecast for the Maritimes on January 1, 1878, was "decreasing northerly winds to westerly winds, clearing and colder weather." Distributing these forecasts, however, was anything but simple: getting the weather word out usually meant sending the lat-est forecast by telegraph. On receipt, the person in charge would arrange to post, for public inspection, the forecasts in a framed bulletin board outside the local telegraph office, post office, school or railway station. In the United States, some communities, besides posting daily forecasts, used flag signals, steam whistles, searchlights and even sirens and bombs to advise people of approaching bad or severe weather.

Most afternoon newspapers in large cities began publishing the tele-graphed weather bulletins as soon as they became available. At first they were only a recitation of the previous day's highs and lows across the country; later they offered predictions and weather maps.

For farming communities along rail lines between Windsor and Halifax, an ingenious system was developed in 1884 to get the weather word out. After receiving a morning dispatch from the central weather office in Toronto, railway agents affixed large metal discs—the shape depended on the approaching weather system—to the engine or bag-gage cars. To farmers working their fields, a full moon chugging by sig-nalled sunny skies, a crescent moon meant showers and a star meant prolonged rainy periods.

Operators at 35 warning stations at ports and harbours along the Great Lakes, St. Lawrence River and Atlantic seaboard used a similar method to warn sailors of approaching gales. The system of cautionary storm signals was quite simple. The central office in Toronto sent warn-ings to the signal stations. Operators at the headlands to the ports or harbours acknowledged the message by return telegraph, then raised wicker baskets, cones or drums from a mast or pole, each representing a different weather pattern. This simple system of storm warnings proved so effective that it was not until the 1950s that the last cautionary storm station with its wicker baskets and signal drums was decommissioned.

Although useful, all these early systems were limited by the constraints of time and space. Often forecasts were old news by the time papers were published or a ship's pilot spotted the signal. And too often, workers whose job it was to update the warnings simply never did, or did it too late to make the information worthwhile. Inevitably, people began to question the reliability of the entire system. Furthermore, as weather services began spreading across the country, officials realized that forecasts were reaching only a fraction of the population. For example, southern British Columbia had a weather service in 1894, and Manitoba's service began in 1899. The service in Saskatchewan and Alberta started up in 1903 and in Newfoundland in 1910.

In the 1920s, all that changed with the technological breakthrough of the wireless radio. Like the telegraph 70 years earlier, the radio revolutionized the way weather data were delivered to Canadians. Information could be gathered from hundreds of remote weather stations across the country and transmitted to isolated logging camps, island communities and even ships at sea. By the time news became a central component of radio broadcasts in the mid-1930s, daily national weather forecasts had become standard fare in thousands of Canadian households.

Every day, Canada's weather service produces 1,300 public forecasts for 200 regions and 1,000 aviation forecasts for 175 airports.

In the 1930s, weather forecasts for all of Canada except southern British Columbia were issued twice daily by a staff of four meteorologists at 9:40 a.m. and 9:40 p.m. The forecasts were based on data from about 217 stations across North America and were for the ensuing 36 to 48 hours—and occasionally 60 hours. Forecasts were distributed as widely as possible by traditional means, the daily press and the posting of daily weather maps and bulletins on public buildings, as well as by telephone, government wireless and radio broadcasting stations. In 1935, the weather service provided a daily national weather synopsis and forecast for the 10:35 p.m. Eastern Standard Time broadcasts of the Canadian Radio Commission's Trans-Canada network—the predecessor of the CBC.

During World War II, Canadian and American government officials banned the broadcasting and publishing of public weather information

Launching a weather balloon, with temperature and precipitation instruments trailing, in Toronto, 1911. *Environment Canada*

over North America. Officials did permit some local weather radio broadcasts and weather maps in newspapers. But for security reasons, no mention could be made of fog, visibility, air pressure, wind direction and cloud height. Even baseball announcers were prohibited from commenting on the weather. One announcer was reputed to have told his audience during a rain delay, "Stick your head out the window if you don't understand the reason for suspension of play."

Following the war, radio became the natural avenue for disseminating weather information, because reports could be updated so quickly throughout the day. This continues today. Frequent weather broadcasts are made daily over hundreds of commercial AM or FM radio stations.

Today, there is another type of radio we are likely to find aboard a combine on a Saskatchewan wheat farm, in a lobster boat off the coast of Nova Scotia or in the lodge of a northern Ontario fishing camp—Weatheradio. This is Environment Canada's network of low-power VHF-FM radio stations, which began transmitting a continuous stream of weather reports in 1976. The service provides taped messages of weather watches and warnings, public and marine forecasts and current weather forecasts. Routinely revised programs run on a cycle of 5 to 10 minutes in length. Weatheradio receivers are portable, inexpensive and available from most electronics stores. In addition, some receivers are equipped with a tone signal and or a flashing light to alert users to warnings of severe weather. People who are hearing impaired may tune in with special digital receivers that decode, download and print out the forecasts. This is called the Weathercopy service.

Televised weathercasts have remained the most popular and effective way of disseminating information about the weather ever since they made their Canadian debut on CBLT-TV in Toronto on September 8, 1952. In the early days, broadcasters used grease pencils and puppets as props. Today, most weather segments are illustrated with radar images and computer animation. In 1988, The Weather Network and its French language equivalent, MétéoMédia, became Canada's channels dedicated exclusively to broadcasting weather news. On average, 6.5 million viewers tune in every week. The average time they spend watching the network's programs each time they tune in has jumped from 3.5 minutes five years ago to 8.2 minutes today.

Yet vestiges of the old systems remain. Where telephone operators in farming communities in 1900 read morning forecasts to dozens of local residents, Canadians today call in to the country's dial-a-weather service. Using high-capacity automatic telephone-answering machines, the system responded to more than 50 million queries in 1994.

With the proliferation of Internet services and users, at no other time in our history has as much weather information been available to so many people. Thousands of World Wide Web sites, including Environment Canada's

Robert Fitzroy, considered the father of weather forecasting, developed a weather-warning service in England in 1859. In August 1861, he began sending three-day forecasts to the newspapers —which soon kicked up a storm of criticism. The Royal Society of London considered anyone giving a weather forecast no better than a charlatan. When Fitzroy died in 1865, the Royal Society discontinued all forecasts for a few years. Sailors and farmers were outraged because they had come to depend on these early forecasts.

Environment Canada is one of the largest radio broadcasters in the country. That's Weatheradio, the VHF radio service that broadcasts weather information around the clock and throughout the year. At last count, the Canadian weather service was operating 203 Weatheradio transmitters, including 19 at coast guard stations in British Columbia. Although 95 percent of Canadians are within range of a Weatheradio transmitter, only about 5 percent have the special VHF receivers needed to pick up the signal.

Green Lane, have been launched with the sole purpose of providing better and more convenient broadcasting products. Several commercial online servers also feature a wealth of weather offerings. You can view or download the latest radar and satellite images, updates on tropical storms and hurricanes and full-colour surface weather maps—the same ones you see on your television weathercast. Or you can download a map and zoom in on a particular area, or store vast amounts of historical climate information. You can also join world-wide discussions with hundreds of other people on various weather topics from the reason for record high dew points in Iowa to storm-chasing experiences in the tornado alley of Oklahoma and Texas.

With the increased speed of microprocessors, weather enthusiasts can now marshal the same specific tools as practising meteorologists. Using a laptop computer, a farmer or fisher living in Cape Breton can follow a hurricane's progress as it spirals up the east coast of the United States, and make a well-informed decision about whether to hunker down and wait out the gale, or pack up and dash for the safety of higher ground.

My Favourite Internet Sites

1. Environment Canada's Green Lane
   http://www.doe.ca/weather_e.html
   Averages more than one million visits a month. Offers current weather observation for major cities, up-to-date weather forecasts for next two days and outlooks for the next five days (no guarantees though), ultraviolet indices, ozone reports, smog forecasts and advisories.

2. The Weather Network
   http://www.theweathernetwork.com
   Offers similar information as the Environment Canada site, plus summaries of weather and environmental news stories from Canada and the world. Click on Explore Weather and get great weather answers from the Expert, too.

3. The Weather Channel
   http://www.weather.com
   Features current weather data from around the world.

4. Bad Meteorology
   http://www.ems.psu.edu/ fraser/BadMeteorology.html
   Examples of bad meteorology and weather myths. Unfortunately, the site goes several months without new material.

5. The Old Farmer's Almanac
   http://www.almanac.com/today/answer.html
   A wealth of useful and useless information, just like the booklet. I especially like the Q and A's on weather and astronomy.

6. FAQ: Hurricanes, Typhoons and Tropical Cyclones
   http://www.aoml.noaa.gov/hrd
   For everything you ever wanted to know about tropical storms, click on AOML/Hurricane. Features hundreds of names for naming your next child. A very active site; especially handy from August to October.

7. Storm Track's Storm Chase Guide
   http://www.telepath.com/storm/chasfaq.htm
   Imperative reading for anyone thinking of spending weekends chasing storms.

8. Monthly and Seasonal Forecasts from Canadian Meteorological Centre
   http://www.cmc.doe.ca/cmc/htmls/forecasts.html
   At the first and fifteenth day of the month, Environment Canada lists their 30-day temperature outlook. Not a weather forecast but an outlook—i.e., how much above or below normal it will be.

9. Climate Trends and Variations Bulletin for Canada
   http://www.tor.ec.gc.ca/ccrm/bulletin
   Description of seasonal temperature and precipitation anomalies for Canada and various regions and how these departures rank against those from the past 50 years.

10. NASA Goddard Institute for Space Studies—Global Temperature Anomalies
    http://www.giss.nasa.gov/Data/GISTEMP/GLB.Ts.txt
    To keep track of global warming—monthly, seasonal and annual global temperature changes over the past century and a half.

11. U.S. National Weather Service
    http://www.nws.noaa.gov
    Hot site for current weather forecasts and charts. What I most like are links to climatic data through the National Climatic Data Center.

Weather Observing and Forecasting

During the 1997 Manitoba flood, two men with a boatful of sandbags passed by a house local residents were trying to save in St. Norbert. *Tom Hanson/Canapress*

"And now for the weather ..."

Many people may remember the debut of Canadian television in September 1952. Among the stars of CBLT-TV in Toronto were the meteorologist Percy Saltzman, a puppet named Uncle Chichimus and his two furry friends, Pompey and Hollyhock. Each night the foursome would do a little skit, preview the evening's programs and finish up with the weather. The puppets were eventually dropped from the show, but Saltzman continued forecasting the weather for 22 years—20 years with the CBC and 2 years with Global—his place in Canadian broadcasting history assured as the first live weatherman to appear on our television screens.

For fans of early Canadian television, Saltzman was "Mr. Weather." His fast-talking, chalk-tossing, anything-goes weather forecast style earned him a legion of fans from Kenora, Ontario, to Quebec City and a faithful American audience just across the border. Somehow, after Saltzman gave the weather forecast, viewers felt they knew what tomorrow would bring and how the weather worked.

Television weather presenting has changed dramatically since the no-frills days when the tools of the trade were chalk and blackboards: high tech then meant magic markers and magnetic smiling suns. Today, computer graphics have revolutionized the industry. Weathercasters no longer have to draw their charts by hand or use stick-on symbols or marker boards. Instead, all television stations have an array of commercially available animation and data-presentation software to enhance the appearance and add interest and value to the weather. Stations woo viewers by boasting the latest in weather tools and electronic gadgetry: three-dimensional clouds tracked by satellites, colour radar imagery and a set replete with banks of monitors and instruments that look like they came from the *Starship Enterprise*.

Most television presenters use a special effect called a chroma-key panel. The person pretends to point at a weather map that is really a large blank wall—an area of green or blue painted plywood or felt board. The weather map or graphic exists in the computer inside the control booth. The camera senses the chroma-key colour and electronically superimposes the graphic on the wall. Then right on cue, the weathercaster clicks through a fast-paced assortment of colourful and informative maps and graphics. Hosts know where to point by looking out the corner of their eyes at TV monitors on each side of the wall or on the camera in front. Skilled presenters can create the illusion that they are touching real maps.

Technology aside, forecasts are still only as accurate as the information that goes into them. Weathercasters, both in Canada and the United States, are not bound to follow the official weather service forecast. Many make their own interpretations, often by just altering the timing of approaching weather or by changing rain to snow. Almost all Canadian weathercasters rely on Environment Canada for current conditions and forecasts (often without any credit). Many tune in to The Weather Network or CNN and listen to Weatheradio. Some stations hire a private weather service to interpret data and provide a forecast tailored to their viewing area.

An effective television weathercast depends largely on the presenter. A good weather broadcaster must be a jack of all trades—a forecaster, computer technician, educator, journalist, psychologist and entertainer. Among the necessary qualities for wannabe weathercasters are personality, enthusiasm, authority and a sense of humour. Above all, it requires someone with good communication skills to present relatively dry scientific information in an engaging way

A woman in Israel sued a television station and its popular weathercaster in small-claims court for the equivalent of almost $1,400 after he predicted sun for a day it rained. The woman claimed his forecast caused her to leave home lightly dressed. The unmentioned rain shower messed up her hair, gave her a case of the flu, which made her miss four days of work, and caused her mental distress. More insulting than the financial compensation sought was the woman's demand that the forecaster apologize for his errors. The court dismissed the case.

that gives the public what they need to know. At the same time, because weather is much more than rain or shine, they must be able to explain succinctly and clearly how the weather systems behave and why.

While an estimated 50 percent or more of television weathercasters in the United States are professional meteorologists or have a science degree, program managers in Canada believe that you don't need to be a meteorologist to know which way the wind is blowing. Apart from a half dozen weather presenters with formal meteorological training, notably Jay Campbell of Channel 10 in London, Claire Martin and Bill Matheson of ITV in Edmonton, Peter Coade of the Atlantic Satellite Network in Halifax, Harold Hosein at Toronto's CityTV and Jocelyne Blouin at Société Radio-Canada in Montreal, most weathercasters have learned forecasting on the job.

Unlike news readers, weather personalities can put their own personal stamp on their telecasts. Some read poems or riddles on air, while many show viewers' photographs or children's drawings. Others, like Sylvia Kuzyk of CKY in Winnipeg and Mike Roberts of CHBC in Kelowna, B.C., have set up a network of volunteer weather spotters or spies who call the station's weather hotline daily. Some weathercasters present the weather outdoors on the street or from the station's roof or patio. Others deliver news of the weather outside from a remote site, sometimes tying it in to a charity event like a TV auction, telethon or celebration. Local boosterism and public-service announcements fit nicely into the weather segment of the newshour.

In the United States, weather shticks and gimmicks abound, as one or two "hippy dippy" weathercasters per market area mix silly antics with isobars and wear outrageous costumes while explaining wind chill. Forecasters have delivered weather reports to live turkeys at Thanksgiving, worn barrels at income-tax deadlines and routinely paraded pets and ridiculous mascots. In Phoenix, Arizona, a French poodle named Puffy Little Cloud would appear wearing an outfit appropriate to the weather—doggy raincoat on wet days and a hand-knitted sweater on chilly ones. No wonder one writer once remarked that "most weathercasters resemble a lounge comedian who did a semester at the Massachusetts Institute of Technology."

Wild and zany weathercasters are the exception in Canada, perhaps

The June 1991 eruption of Mount Pinatubo in the Philippines caused temperatures to fall around the world. Ponopresse

Snowrollers are giant natural snowballs formed by the wind.
R.S. Schemenauer

Sun pillars are most common at sunset or sunrise. R.S. Schemenauer

Ice Storm '98 (*above and right*) left more than
4 million people in Ontario and Quebec without
electricity, some for several weeks. R. Côté/Ponopresse

Paul Norbo

A chinook arch extends northward over Clarsholm, Alberta, towards Calgary. Studio 232 Photography Ltd.

Some 28,000 Manitoba residents were forced to leave their homes during the Red River flood of 1997. Ponopresse

On November 7, 1994, a ferocious windstorm felled 15 million trees in New Brunswick. Jody Gallant/Repap

Percy Saltzman was the first weathercaster to appear on Canadian television. *Herb Nott/CBC*

because we have too much weather, or we take it very seriously. Dave Devall of CFTO in Toronto intrigues viewers by writing backwards on plexiglass. Kuzyk of Winnipeg remembers once swinging onto the set on a tire suspended from the rafters. The acknowledged king of performing Canadian weathercasters is CityTV's Hosein. At various times, he has delivered the weather masquerading as a witch, Dracula, a nutty professor and a cadaver. He has also done the weather while parasailing and lying on the ground with a Frisbee-catching dog leaping over him.

The impetus behind such antics may well be the nature of weather—90 percent of the days aren't exciting or eventful. How many fresh ways can you say "sunny and cold"? When I was a youngster in Windsor, Ontario, my favourite weathercaster was Detroit's Sonny Elliot. For three decades, Sonny's trademark was coining new weather terms—a snowy and breezy day became "sneezy"; showers and windy made for "shindy" conditions; and fog and drizzle produced "frizzle."

What has to be an anomaly in Canadian broadcasting is the incredible longevity of Canadian television presenters—40 years for Bill Matheson in Lethbridge and Edmonton; 30 years for Dave Devall in Toronto. Most remarkable is that these veterans are still on air after putting their credibility on the line five days a week for millions of

---------------------------------►

The Weather Network and its French-language counterpart, MétéoMédia, were launched on September 1, 1988. They currently reach eight million Canadian households on cable from coast to coast through 750 affiliated cable companies. The Weather Network employs a staff of more than 300 technicians, meteorologists and support staff. The network's programs are seen in 85 percent of Canadian homes with cable TV and in 54.7 percent of all households with television. The average time viewers spend watching has jumped from 3-1/2 to 5, to more than 8 minutes daily. At any given moment, at least 33,000 Canadians are tuned in.

viewers to judge.

All television weathercasters are enthusiastic when severe weather threatens. Of course, having the lead story with frequent updates throughout the newscast makes them feel important and needed. And they're right! It's hard to think of a news or sports story that is as crucial to the public as a promptly aired weather advisory.

Unfortunately, weathercasters are too often convenient targets for sarcastic remarks, "Thanks for that *great* day!" or "How come you weather guys never get it right!" In the weather business, you can't please all of the people all of the time. You don't even try! The exasperated farmer from Perth who did not get a shower when all those around him did; the restaurateur with the outdoor patio irate that rain is mentioned yet again; and the anxious skier annoyed by winter's late arrival. Kelowna's affable Mike Roberts has been hanged in effigy for too much rain and too much sun. One woman angrily confronted him for forecasting isolated showers. She thought it meant ice showers and worried every time he mentioned them. One viewer wanted Hosein fired because he claimed the weathercaster was always wrong. And a trailer-camp operator threatened to sue Bill Matheson of CITV in Edmonton because he predicted rainy weather when the day turned out beautiful and sunny. Believe it or not, weathercasters have even been accused of creating the weather.

One common complaint, justified at times, is the tendency of weathercasters to pack too many weather details into four minutes, droning on about fronts and troughs, dew point and barometric pressure. This can be particularly annoying when all you want to know is whether it's going to rain tomorrow. Also, why must they show a map with temperatures from 100 nearby locales that are no more than 1°C apart?

As for weathercasters, one of their grievances is snoozing anchors. It's bad enough being the brunt of stale one-liners every night and having the co-hosts and crew vacate the set when the weather segment comes up. But it is annoying to hear the anchor say, "Great, looking forward to a weekend of fine weather," when you have just forecast two days of overcast skies with showers.

Television weather presenters should demand more time from program managers and more respect from both their colleagues and the public. Audience studies in every major market consistently show that the television weathercast is one of the main reasons why people tune into local news. Ratings for weathercasters are way ahead of sports and even above the top news story.

In 1998 Percy Saltzman turns 82 years old. Still recognized on Toronto streets by his fans, and ever the fast-talking, quick wit that he was 40 years ago, Percy says he's not interested in television weather. If he needs to know what's happening, he looks out the window—just what he hated to hear when he was called Mr. Weather.

A viewer once wrote Percy Saltzman saying, "I don't like the weather, but my cat watches you." On another occasion, Eric Nielson, MP for Yukon, objected in Parliament that by showing very cold temperatures in Yukon, Percy was giving the territory a bad name.

The four-minute weather segment looks simple enough but usually takes hours of preparation and is often more predictable than the weather itself. For Jay Campbell of CFPL in London, Ontario, a typical day begins at 5:30 a.m. and doesn't end until the spotlights shut off at 7 p.m. From his home, Campbell monitors radio and television broadcasts and logs on to his computer to tap in to weather circuits from around the Great Lakes. For his noon telecast on CFPL, Campbell usually arrives at the studio at 8:30 a.m., earlier if severe weather is occurring or expected. The next couple of hours is spent poring over stacks of general and local forecasts and maps he receives from Environment Canada, the National Weather Service in the United States and several private weather-forecasting services. Soon, Campbell begins to put together a picture of what the weather is going to be like across southern Ontario and develops his own forecast. Much of the time is spent creating graphics and satellite and radar animations. A typical sequence on air includes satellite loops; current weather map with fronts, highs, lows and icons for significant weather; an almanac of highs, lows, normals and records; a regional forecast and temperature maps for the afternoon and overnight; and a five-day outlook. About a half hour before air, Campbell makes a final call to the weather office to get the latest readings from around the province. At noon, he is on air delivering a 10-second weather tease against a live shot from any one of several remote sites. Twenty-five minutes later, he's back on for four minutes, live and unscripted, with current conditions and the day's forecast, followed at 12:55 p.m. with an update and a three-city five-day weather outlook. At 4:30 p.m., preparations begin for the six o'clock evening news. Fitting in talks at schools and to community groups, and answering countless questions makes for a full day.

METEOROLOGICAL
MUMBO JUMBO

What could be so perfectly comprehensible as: *sunny with a few cloudy periods; windy with the chance of an afternoon shower; warmer; high 25?*

However, almost all the everyday words that the weather forecaster uses are at times vague, complex or ambiguous. *Bright, clear, intermittent, variable cloudiness* and *likelihood* all give rise to misinterpretation.

A weather forecast, to be useful, has to be clear, specific and impersonal, and should be worded in such a way that millions of people instantly understand it. People prefer the weather presented in conversational terms. They are befuddled by terms such as *trowal, trough* and *tephigram.*

And it should be concise: people can absorb and remember only so much information at one time. Most people simply want to know whether it is going to rain or snow today, not where the cold front was three days ago. One survey found that more than half of those who watch a weather report on television cannot recall where or how much it is expected to rain, even seconds after the forecast has been given. We may all hear the same forecast, but we often come away with a different message. Mind you, some weathercasters' antics, jabber, visual wizardry and gimmicks can obscure the essential message.

In the end, the value of an accurate forecast hinges on how well it is understood. But has the average person the same conception of weather and weather terms as the meteorologist? Qualifiers such as *intermittent, variable, occasional* and *scattered* have unmistakable meaning to forecasters, but they may convey something quite different to the public. *Fair* weather may mean clear skies to one person, but merely the absence of rain to another. Even though a forecast is issued, and later verified, it is often deemed either a bust by the general public, or even worse, it is misinterpreted. The consequences can range from merely bothersome (you plan a picnic based on what seemed like a good forecast, but it rains) to life threatening (being caught on a golf course in a thunderstorm). Such incidents hurt the weather forecaster's credibility. Besides being the most maligned, they become the most misquoted of human beings.

Sometimes people seem to remember only what they want to hear. *Partly sunny* may be recollected as *sunny.* And a forecast that calls for a "30 percent possibility of rain" may be seen as misinformation if it doesn't rain, if the element of probability is overlooked.

Several phrases used in official forecasts are often confused or misunderstood. Do you know what a 70 percent probability of rain means? In a national survey, only 10 percent of respondents knew it meant that on 7 days out of 10 with a similar weather pattern, a given place with-

---

Partly Sunny?

Partly sunny and *partly cloudy* are among the most poorly understood of all weather terms. Forecasters have been debating the definition of *partly* for years; that's why it is not widely used. In forecasting sky conditions, meteorologists describe what percentage of the sky, from horizon to horizon, rounded to the nearest 10, is expected to be covered by clouds.

* A *sunny* day is one with no clouds or only 10 percent of the sky is expected to have cloud
* With 20 percent or 30 percent cloud, the forecast calls for *mostly* or *mainly sunny*, or *sunny with cloudy periods*
* When more cloud than sun is forecast, say 70 to 80 percent cloud, it's *mostly* or *mainly cloudy* or *cloudy with clear periods*
* When 90 percent or more of the full sky is covered by cloud, then it's a *cloudy or overcast* sky
* When it's about half cloud and half blue sky, the wording is *mix of sun and clouds* or *variable cloudiness*

---

in the forecast area (your house or the airport, for example) will receive measurable rainfall (0.2 millimetres or more). In simpler terms, a probability of precipitation forecast (POP) is just what it sounds like—an expression of the forecaster's confidence that there will be rain or snow. If there is a good chance, the forecaster may say 80 percent; if dry weather is expected, the POP may be 20 percent.

Meteorologists do worry about whether the public fully understands their forecasts. Studies in Canada and the United States over the past 50 years indicate that most people understand most of the terms in daily forecasts. However, differences do exist between the meteorological meanings of some expressions and how people perceive them. To reduce the confusion, a few words have been abandoned, existing ones revised and new ones formulated.

Fortunately for the public, much of the meteorologist's specialized vocabulary never makes it into official forecasts. Visit a weather office and you'll hear conversations peppered with such technical terms as *cold low, dry tongue* and *helicity*. Then there are everyday words with special meanings, such as *waves*—as in cold wave—or *front* in the sense of a surface where masses of warm and cold air come into conflict. Over the years, a variety of other meteorological mumbo jumbo has crept into the forecaster's lingo, if not into the official public forecast, such as *dead clouds*, *bombs* and *busts*, and *suckerholes* and *hot boxes*, to name a few. Meteorology is not without word play—*flicker factor*, *dingbat deepener*, *cirrusnirrus* and *severe clear*—and abbreviations, including *TTTC* for weather that is "too tough to call." On the other hand, the origin of some words is no mystery, although the context may be: Alberta clipper, Colorado hooker and Texas gully washer.

Some weather words really don't mean what they may seem to. For example, *cloud cover* is really sky cover, *zero visibility* includes visibility up to a distance of below 100 metres, *probability* doesn't mean probable, and *meteorology* has nothing to do with meteors.

Some words have been retired from use in public forecasts. For example, you no longer see the expression *unsettled weather* in an official public forecast. At one time, it meant brief periods of fine weather alternating with periods of rainy, cloudy or stormy weather, a kind of variable weather. As the retired Halifax meteorologist Reuben Hornstein explained, "The public joked that a forecast of unsettled weather might mean either that the weather was going to be extremely changeable, or that the forecaster was unsettled about what to forecast and took refuge in that rather vague and indeterminate wording."

Another word banned from official forecasts is *fair*, once used to describe days with sunny intervals, or warm and pleasant days without sunshine. Following much public criticism that it was vague, the term was dropped from the forecaster's slate of official weather words. Likewise, *cloudy with sunny periods* and *sunny with cloudy periods* are not

> **Thunderstorms or thunder snows are fairly rare in eastern Canada in the winter, occurring maybe once each season, although they often go undetected. In western Canada, winter thunderstorms are very rare, with some cities such as Edmonton and Saskatoon reporting only one in the past 30 years.**

Some Newfoundland Weather Terms:

airsome	cold, fresh, bracing
civil	no wind
dally	sudden lull
dwye	gust, flurry, squall on the coasts, brief shower or storm
faffering	blowing in sudden gusts
fairy squall	strong sudden gusts of wind on a calm day
flaw	sudden gust of wind
hog's nose	waterspout
in wind	wind blowing from sea to shore; reverse to out wind
liner	high wind at time of equinox
lun	winds die down
norther	a furious cold wind from the north
screecher	a howling storm
scud	wind gust
scuddy	misty showery; sudden gusts
sheila's brush/blush	fierce storm and heavy snowfall about March 18
shuff	gust of wind
smoke	gusts of wind and spray
stun breeze	20 to 25 knot sea wind
weatherish	sky clouding over and looking weatherish

permitted because few people understand the shades of meaning between them. Environment Canada allows phrases such as *mainly sunny, mainly cloudy* and *variable cloudiness*, but prefers just plain *sunny* or *cloudy*.

Subjective comments such as *fine* are also considered inappropriate—sunny weather may be great news for resort owners or construction companies, but it could be a disaster for farmers hoping for drought-ending rains.

Some widely used words are not part of the meteorologist's vernacular. For example, Environment Canada never adopted the term *sleet*, which was once used in the United States to describe solid grains of ice formed by raindrops freezing before contact with the ground. They bounce and make a sound upon impact. In Canada, we call them ice pellets. In the United Kingdom, sleet means something entirely different—rain and snow falling together, or snow that melts as it meets the ground.

Even expressions coined by meteorologists to make a weather concept more comprehensible are open to misinterpretation. One example is *wind chill*, used to describe what cold weather feels like at various combinations of low temperatures and high winds. The problem is that some people confuse it with the actual temperature. Moreover, the formula used to calculate wind chill doesn't take into account factors such as incoming and outgoing radiation, sunshine, humidity and human metabolic rate—important elements in how acutely individuals feel the cold. Adding to the confusion, wind chill is expressed differently across the country. In Manitoba and Saskatchewan, the cooling rate is commonly given in watts per square metre or as a plain number without a unit of measurement. In Ontario and Quebec, residents prefer to have wind chill conveyed as the equivalent temperature in degrees Celsius. And in Atlantic Canada, people prefer a verbal description of wind chill or its effects, such as *bitterly cold*, *extremely cold* or *exposed flesh will freeze in one minute*.

Some weather expressions are used only in specific regions or provinces. *Chinooks* are the dry, warm winds from the west that occur principally in southern Alberta; and in Newfoundland, a *silver thaw* or *glitter* refers to a freezing rainstorm. To better serve regional needs, local forecasters have some flexibility in their choice of terminology and forecasting criteria. For example, the Quebec Weather Centre in Montreal issues a severe wind warning when sustained winds of at least 50 kilometres an hour or gusts of 90 kilometres an hour or more are forecast. By contrast, the Alberta Weather Centre issues a severe wind warning for the Lethbridge area—where chinooks are prevalent—only if sustained winds of 70 kilometres per hour or gusts of 120 kilometres per hour are expected.

An icebow is produced the same way as a rainbow, but through ice crystals, not raindrops. Because there are not as many crystals as drops, and the colours are not spread out as much, icebows are generally white. Ordinary snowflakes cannot produce rainbows, so true snowbows are not possible. What we sometimes mistake for snowbows are sundogs.

The following is a sampling of meteorologists' jargon:

- *Alberta clipper:* a rapidly moving storm that streaks out of the Prairies across central and southern Ontario, often leaving a dusting of snow
- *bust:* unforeseen and not forecast weather; called a bomb or gremlin in the United States

Weather warnings are issued in Canada for heavy snow, blizzards, snow squalls, wind, freezing rain, heavy rain, flash freeze, winter storms, wind chill, a cold wave, severe thunderstorms, tornadoes, dust storms and frost.

- *cirrusnirrus:* thin, wispy, high cirrus cloud that forewarns of an approaching storm
- *cold low:* a weather system that consists of a low-pressure area riding above a mass of cold air at the earth's surface, bounded by slowly swirling bands of cloud and precipitation in the upper atmosphere
- *Colorado hooker:* a storm that originates over the eastern plains of Colorado and moves across the Central Plains and Mississippi Valley; the storm taps moisture from the Gulf of Mexico and pulls cold air down from Canada; it's hooked, or curved, path sometimes brings it into southern Canada, where it dumps heavy snow
- *dead clouds:* cumulus clouds that blot out the sun but are usually incapable of generating precipitation
- *dingbat deepener:* a storm centre that intensifies rapidly (roughly 2 kPa in 24 hours)
- *flicker factor* (used in Ontario): if electric lights on the northern horizon appear to flicker in the evening, then fog is unlikely overnight; if there is no flicker, the atmosphere favours the formation of fog
- *helicity:* a measure of the potential of a small area of the atmosphere to spin rapidly, forming a tornado; expressed as a number, it is used to describe the danger of tornadoes forming within individual thunderstorms
- *hot box:* a localized storm area squared off on a weather map for which a meteorologist is likely to issue severe storm warnings; helicity is often closely monitored within hot boxes

A Guide to Probability of Precipitation:

Canadian forecasters commonly use POP, probability of precipitation, in their forecasts. A probability of 60 percent doesn't mean that it will rain 60 percent of the day, or that rain will fall on 60 percent of your area. It also says nothing about how much rain or snow will occur. A POP of 60 percent means that the forecasters have calculated that in 100 similar weather situations, rain has fallen 60 times at any specified point in the forecast area.

0%	No precipitation, even though it may be cloudy
10%	Dry weather with only one chance in 10 of snow or rain falling
30%	Go ahead with your picnic, boating or ski plans, but you may have to take shelter
40%	An umbrella is recommended; make alternative plans for outdoor activities that are susceptible to rain; not a good day to pave the driveway; keep your fingers crossed
50%	It's even Steven whether it snows/rains; be prepared for all eventualities
60%	Want to water your lawn? The odds are favourable that Mother Nature may give you some help
70%	Suggest cancellation of outside events; the chances for dry weather have shrunk to 3 in 10
80%	Wet weather likely; make appropriate plans
90%	The occurrence of precipitation is a near certainty; venture out if you enjoy walking in the rain or playing in the snow
100%	Precipitation is a certainty

Adapted from Environment Canada

- *NTW:* short for *not to worry;* weather that is difficult to forecast—say, an indeterminate range of cloudiness or temperature—but that poses no danger
- *prairie schooner:* follows the same path as an Alberta clipper, but much slower and capable of dropping more snow
- *severe clear:* not a cloud in the sky
- *suckerhole:* a brief period of clear weather that lasts until just after the good weather forecast has been issued or until a pilot flying without instruments takes off; only a sucker amends the forecast to reflect the good weather, and only a sucker flies with-

out instruments when such conditions occur
- *Texas gully washer:* rain intense enough to flood gullies
- *TTTC:* weather that is "too tough to call"

A WILD WINTER IS ON THE WAY— MAYBE

When farmer Ed Burt of Gore Bay, Ontario, on Manitoulin Island, spotted a wasps' nest on the cross-arm of a hydro pole in the summer of 1992, he was worried.

Burt is a homegrown weather prophet who believes nature's creatures can foretell weather conditions. The higher off the ground wasps, bees and hornets build their homes, he maintains, the deeper the winter snow will be. And if they build in sheltered areas such as barns and woodsheds, expect a long, harsh winter. In 1993, Burt found three wasps' nests close to the ground. "Sure enough, there was little snow that year," he says. However, he admits the hydro-pole nest signified nothing more than wasps with a penchant for penthouse living; snowfall that winter was below normal.

Gordon Restoule is another believer. He operates a tourist camp on the Dokis Indian Reserve southwest of North Bay, Ontario. For him, it's the thickness of mud that beavers plaster on their lodges that reveals the misery level of the coming winter: the more mud, the worse the winter. Geese flying south early and high up promise a rough winter too, he says. Restoule claims 80 percent accuracy, but acknowledges he blew it the winter of 1993–94 when he predicted a mild winter and it turned out to be the coldest in nearly 75 years.

In Alberta, Roy Robertson, a retired farmer and former trapper who now works in season as a greens keeper at the Grande Prairie golf course, keeps his eye on woodlot denizens. If squirrels are frantically storing cones and mushrooms, look for a cold snowy winter, he declares. Expect a warmer one with little snow if beavers are late starting their winter feed

The wild icy winter of '98 in Quebec and eastern Ontario won't soon be forgotten. *Robert Galbraith/Canapress*

beds, or if elk and moose are late in mating. Mind you, says the soft-spoken former trapper, "Nature throws the odd curve! I missed the heavy snow last winter, but it didn't matter much, because I spent the season in Arizona."

Homey weather wisdom has been the basis for weather predictions for thousands of years. People whose livelihoods depended on the environment observed the regular patterns of nature: changing of the seasons, the sun's daily progress, the moon phases, animal hibernations and bird migrations. If these things followed a set course, they reasoned, weather should too. For many of these weather pundits, the annual meteorological event of greatest economic and social importance was the severity or mildness of the approaching winter.

Today, most meteorologists scoff at weather superstitions, claiming they lack scientific validity. Long-range proverb meteorology, they say, is simply not all right for all times in all places. They *are* silly or foolish notions; however, these light-hearted fancies are fun to repeat and wonder about. They bring public renown to their creators. That's why there is no shortage of long-range weather prophets and believers.

Nonetheless, many naturalists have long subscribed to the theory

Some Foreign Winter Weatherlore

- When the hare's coat is thick, the winter will be hard (Germany).
- A heavy November snow will last till April (U.S.A. and France).
- Snowy winter, rainy summer; icy winter, hot summer (Russia).
- White Christmas, green Easter; green Christmas, white Easter (Belgium).
- When the leaves of wheat are narrow and short, there will be much snow (Japan).
- Long icicles foretell a long spring (Russia).
- Mushrooms galore, much snow in store; no mushrooms at all, no snow will fall (Germany, U.S.A.).
- If the first thunder is from the east, the winter is over (New Mexico).
- Autumn thunder means a mild winter (Norway).
- If cattle and sheep after fruit-laden autumn dig the ground and strain their heads towards the north wind, then expect a very stormy winter (New Zealand).
- When gnats swarm in January, the peasant will have an empty granary (Netherlands).
- Mosquitoes in late fall, a mild winter for all (Russia).
- The 12 days after Christmas will indicate the weather for each of the following months (Choctaw Indians, West Virginia).

that certain animals and insects have instincts and sensitivities that make them trustworthy forecasters. One such example is the woolly bear caterpillar famous for its forecasting prowess, especially after its cameo appearance several years ago on "The Tonight Show." Superstition has it that if the brown stripes are narrower than the black, winter will be cold and blustery. Science, however, says the width of the stripes is determined more by a combination of genetics and environmental conditions when the insect is growing rather than indicative of any privileged insider information.

There is also a widespread belief that an abnormally thick coat of fur on beavers, dogs, bears and other animals forewarns a grim winter. An animal may well grow a heavier coat if October is especially cold, but that does not necessarily mean the entire winter will be harsh. Again, it's more likely a matter of diet, health and day length prior to the onset of winter.

> When squirrels early start to hoard
> Winter will pierce us like a sword.

In a similar vein, there is no connection between the number of cones and mushrooms a hungry squirrel or chipmunk tucks away in the fall and the coming winter's severity. Most just tuck away as much as they can in the best hiding place they can find. A large cache may indicate nothing more than a favourable harvest that year. Nor is there any connection between deep snows and places where harvesting creatures store their booty—high up in trees or deep in the ground.

Farmers often turn to their own barnyard animals as weather soothsayers. Pigs and backyard geese have long served as a farmer's weather vane. Ed Burt relies on the shape of the spleen of a freshly butchered pig, as his father and grandfather did before him. "A thick bulge at one end that tapers off means winter will be short," he explains. "No bulge means an even winter, and an extra wide bulge along the spleen expect a very cold winter." A cold winter with a mild spell is indicated if the bulge is irregular, he adds.

Then, there's the Thanksgiving turkey. According to legend, if half the breast of a cooked Thanksgiving turkey is brown and half white, winter will first be cold, but will warm up in January or February. Other turkey lore suggests that a thin breastbone means a mild winter, a thick bone a severe winter, a light bone more snow but a mild winter, and a dark bone signals colder temperatures are on the way. This last claim is not without merit, for the dark colour means that the bird has absorbed a lot of oil, a natural protection against the cold.

Hunters and fishers notice natural omens too. Anglers will tell you to prepare for a bad winter if trout feed voraciously in the fall to gain weight. Hunters pay attention to early southbound geese, the thickness and strength of waterfowl feathers and how far down a partridge's leg its

Some Plant Winter Weatherlore

- Extremely tall weeds in the summer are supposed to mean we'll be doing a lot of shovelling.
- The thickness of corn husks in the fall is said to be proportional to the degree of winter cold, and a double husk is said to forebode a winter of exceptional severity. Tall corn stalks are proportional to the depth of the coming winter snowfall.
- When leaves fall early, fall and winter will be mild; when leaves fall late, winter will be severe. If trees hang on to their leaves, the coming winter will be cold.

feathers extend, all to determine winter's clout.

Plants and trees are sensitive to weather and its changes, but they can only convey something about past and present circumstances of growing, nothing about the future.

> Onion skins very thin
> Mild winters coming in.
> Onion skins thick and tough
> Coming winter cold and rough.

The fact that an onion has many thick skins does not mean that it will be a hard winter, but merely that certain conditions of heat and moisture occurred while it was growing.

Still, folklorists see portents in the supply of fruit on shrubs and trees in the fall. They believe nature provides an extra store of berries to feed the birds when deep snows are in the offing. If a bad winter lies ahead, birds will leave the berries on the bushes till the snow comes; if a mild one is coming, they will gobble them up. The reality, of course, is that favourable flowering weather prevailed during pollination and so ensured an ample berry crop.

Another method of seasonal weather divining involves the principles of persistence and compensation, which are reflected in folk proverbs. In the what-you-get category are:

A foggy autumn will be followed by a soggy winter.
As the weather in October, so will be the next March.
Fall thunder means a mild winter.

In the nature-seeks-a-balance category:

Rainy summer, snowy winter
Hot summer, icy winter.
A month that comes in bad goes out bad.
When there is a spring in the winter, or a winter in the spring, the year is never good.

Analyses of lengthy climate records fail to disclose any relationship between summer and winter weather. The only long-term weather sayings with any truth are the cause and effect ones, such as:
A year of snow, a year of plenty.

Or, phrased differently:

A year of snow, crops will grow.

These are pleasant ways of pointing out that a snowy winter provides enough moisture to assure good crops, and that a good covering of snow insulates crops against killing cold and the cycles of thawing and freezing, especially ruinous to winter grains.
One more maxim that works because it is logical is:

As the days lengthen, so the cold strengthens.

This simply recognizes that January and February are usually the coldest months, even though the days are lengthening after the December 21 solstice.
Giving nature a run for its money in long-range predictions is that "red book" of weather wisdom, the country, or farmer's almanac. Popular for generations, these little publications purport to know what

---

Some Animal Winter Weatherlore

- When bees close their hives, a cold winter arrives; if they don't shut the door, a mild winter's in store.
- When you see a beaver carrying sticks in its mouth, it will be a hard winter.
- Muskrats building houses early indicate a tough winter.
- Wild geese moving south: cold weather ahead; moving north: winter is nearly over.
- A bad winter is betide, if hair grows thick on a bear's hide.
- If yellowjackets start acting clumsy and crickets sing their last song as the new moon rises, winter will be early.

---

the weather will be for an entire year, supposedly by using secret formulas to blend information on moon phases, tides and sunspots with astrological rules and climatological data. Their credibility springs from people focusing on unusual events, and remembering the successes and forgetting the failures. Furthermore, the weather somewhere on any given day is bound to turn out exactly as called for in at least one almanac.

So, what can we expect for next winter? The folks like Ed Burt, Gordon Restoule and Roy Robertson have already taken note. Look out, Canada, a wild and woolly winter may be just around the corner. And, surely one edition of the farmer's almanac says so!

STORM CHASING

As a youngster, Pat McCarthy spent many hours watching summer storms develop near his home in Gibbons, Alberta, northeast of Edmonton. When threatening black skies sent most of his family indoors, McCarthy often stayed out to photograph the angry clouds until rain or hail would chase him in. When he was old enough, he would follow storms in the family car.

Now a meteorologist with Environment Canada in Winnipeg, McCarthy still makes a hobby of tracking and trailing Prairie storms. Seven years ago, realizing that hunting storms by himself could be dangerous, McCarthy and two fellow storm chasers convinced 15 other meteorologists from the weather office in Winnipeg to join them in their pursuit. Thus began the Fighting Prairie Weather Dogs, a group of dedicated storm chasers looking for adventure and a greater understanding of how tornadoes and other severe weather systems behave. McCarthy says they chose the name because "prairie dogs are often seen near their burrows, sitting and watching for hazards." The group's ultimate goal is to save lives by issuing earlier warnings of severe weather.

Storm chasing is not a new pursuit. It began among meteorologists using airplanes in the United States in 1948. Ground-based chasing took hold in the 1950s, when the network of paved roads expanded, enabling storm chasers to move faster than most storms, which typically travel at speeds below the posted limit. One of the first successful ground-based chases occurred on May 24, 1973, when scientists from the U.S. National Weather Service and the University of Oklahoma intercepted and issued warnings of a tornado west of Oklahoma City. For the first time, meteorologists were able to record the entire life cycle of a tornado on film and Doppler radar.

In recent years, chasing storms has developed into a craze, crowding the highways on weekends with amateur spotters and television news teams, some in helicopters. Armed with video cameras, thrill seekers and adrenaline junkies prowl the central United States hoping to capture spectacular weather footage to sell to network television, seeking fame and fortune by selling videotapes and photographs.

Few regions in the world are safe from tornadoes. Each year, the United States averages about 1,000 tornadoes. Canada rates second in the world for tornado occurrence, with more than 80, followed by Russia with 60, Great Britain 40, Australia 15 and Italy 10. Twisters occur in many parts of Europe, India, China, Japan, Bermuda, the Fiji Islands and South Africa.

In Canada, several storm teams have taken up the hunt over the years. The first group organized in the late 1970s, when the Alberta Hail Project included a storm-chase program. As for the Fighting Prairie Weather Dogs, each year from May to August, these intrepid storm troopers drive hundreds of kilometres to catch a tornado ... on film. Although the big catch has eluded them, the Weather Dogs boast many photographs and useful videotapes of severe summer storms.

Only 2 percent of all tornadoes are considered "violent," with wind speeds of 480 kilometres per hour. However, violent tornadoes cause 70 percent of all tornado deaths.

The eastern Prairies—where the Weather Dogs are based—is an ideal location to watch for storms. It's big-sky country—clear and open—without the haze and pollution of industrial regions, and away from the obstruction of mountains. On the relatively flat terrain, the details of distant clouds and the formation of tornadoes can be readily seen.

The Prairies also favour the development of severe storms. In summer, air descending over the eastern slopes of the Rockies warms and dries out as it sinks, creating hot, dry cloud-free air. As the air continues eastward towards lower elevations, it mixes with tongues of warm, moist air from the Gulf of Mexico and cold, dry air from the north, triggering fierce thunderstorms. As a storm builds higher in altitude, the overriding jet stream strengthens its updraft. This produces towering clouds that may begin to rotate, leading to tornadoes dropping from the sky.

In an average summer, 10 tornadoes occur in Manitoba and 16 in Saskatchewan. These figures pale compared with the tornado alley of western Oklahoma and the Texas Panhandle where on average 65 tornadoes are spotted annually, making it a hot spot for chasing and catching a tornado. A somewhat envious McCarthy says that the chance of seeing a twister in Oklahoma is one in seven. On the Prairies, the odds are much lower. During the warm season, tornadoes in Canada average one every five days; to the south, where tornadoes are almost routine, they average five every day.

"Everyone asks why do I do it," says McCarthy. "I know some of my relatives think I'm foolish, and there are meteorologists who don't understand why chasing storms can be so compelling." All serious storm chasers have a healthy respect and abiding curiosity for summer storms. It's not just thrill seeking. Storm chasers have contributed greatly to our understanding of the structure and movement of summer storms and the conditions likely to produce them. Photographing and observing summer storms has also been useful for training severe-weather watchers and familiarizing the public with the appearance of extreme summer storms.

Storm chasing involves much more than hopping in a car and watching the sky. One of the Weather Dogs' storm coordinators alerts other members to the possibility of severe weather the day before, and preparations for the chase get under way immediately. The storm coordinator forms one or two chase teams which ideally comprise three people—a driver, a navigator and a photographer. Each team then lines up a vehicle, buys film, charges the batteries and puts together a storm kit that includes a cellular telephone, still and video cameras, maps, a compass, log sheets and portable weather equipment provided by the weather office—an anemometer to measure wind speed, a rain gauge and thermometers.

The next day, the team heads to the office to check the morning's weather charts, radar scans and satellite images. Meanwhile, the storm coordinator and severe-weather meteorologist monitor the hourly weather changes and pore over the upper-air soundings. A successful chase depends on the coordinator's correctly pinpointing the chase field—the area where a thunderstorm is likely to occur. Then the coordinator must decide if the storm is accessible and within safe driving distance. He or she arrives at a decision, usually by mid-morning, whether to dispatch teams to a designated target area, to put them on standby or simply to call them off.

Once a team gets the go-ahead, the navigator chooses the intercept route on the basis of road availability, visual storm observations and information received from the weather office. The navigator is also responsible for documenting the chase—landmarks, phone calls, starts and stops

Since the "Black Friday" tornado in Edmonton on July 31, 1987, no tornado has killed anyone in Canada, even though between 80 and 100 tornadoes occur on average each year.

and meteorological sightings. The driver's responsibility is to operate the vehicle in a safe and legal fashion—and to pay any traffic tickets. Readying the vehicle for a quick exit is also important.

Storm chasing is largely a driving and waiting game. Inside the car, the team members constantly read the sky for signs of atmospheric change, take weather measurements, keep in touch with the weather office by cellular phone and listen for static on local radio stations that may signal an approaching storm. The talk is often of tail-end Charlies and rear-flank downdrafts, outflows and gustnadoes, and anvils and shears. In many cases, chasers spend hours of frustration and disappointment parked at the side of a country road, often in sultry air and under blue skies, waiting for something to happen that probably won't.

Robert Davies-Jones, director of the tornado-intercept project at the United States National Severe Storms Laboratory in Norman, Oklahoma, estimates that he spends about 200 hours in the field each storm season. "We hope for one or two good days, and in that, two to three good hours. And then it boils down to about 10 minutes, as far as a tornado is concerned. And that's the whole season." Chasers try to convince one another of the good signs—ragged cloud peaks, sharp anvils, emerald green skies, clusters of cumulus towers that appear to grow and die, multiple layers of low and middle clouds racing overhead in different directions and a few drops of rain.

On June 22, 1992, the Weather Dogs were within minutes of witnessing a large tornado that later struck near Morden, Manitoba. "We got on the wrong side of the heavy rain," recalls McCarthy. "To reach the wall cloud where the

Gene "Mad Bomber" Moore is a veteran storm chaser from Oklahoma who has managed to photograph 200 tornadoes. In 1986, he confessed in an article in *Weatherwise* magazine, "I have been bashed by hailstones, hit by lightning, and been inside one tornado." He faced death in 1981 when he got trapped beneath a funnel cloud in Nebraska. "I did all the wrong things, but got out alive probably only because I was driving a fast sports car. But the coffin was open and waiting."

This tornado touched down in Edmonton on July 31, 1987, killing 27 people and causing more than $250 million damage. *Steve Simon/Canapress*

tornado was likely to pop out would mean driving along muddy roads through blinding rain, so we broke off the chase. It would have been a thrill to see our first tornado from the ground, but we never compromise safety for that one picture." As another veteran storm chaser remarked, "It's just as dangerous to catch a violent storm as it is for one to catch you." Instead, the team went after another storm farther north and managed to shoot a video that clearly shows all the features of severe weather.

Despite the long delays and disappointments, storm chasers can never allow frustration to overcome caution and good sense. Storm chasing can be both difficult and dangerous, and accidents do happen.

Storm chasers consider lightning and hail—not tornadoes—the greatest hazards associated with their hobby. Setting up an aluminum tripod on a hilltop is not a smart thing to do with lightning flashing all around you. Careful chasers minimize the risks by taking photographs from inside their car at the first drops of rain. In 1981, a lightning bolt struck three storm chasers in central Oklahoma. All three survived, but they had headaches for hours afterward. Car accidents are another hazard. In 1984, a graduate student from the University of Oklahoma was killed when his car overturned on a rain-slicked highway while he was pursuing a tornado. As a rule, chasers usually avoid unpaved roads. Dirt roads are just too treacherous when wet.

Other chase rules include these: don't hunt alone; if you can't see the cloud and ground, you are too close; where there is one tornado, there is possibly a second one nearby; and never drive blindly into the precipitation core—there could be a tornado right behind it.

By persevering in the face of these risks, trained storm chasers have contributed most of what we know about the size, speed and internal structure of tornadoes and the conditions likely to produce them. They were the first to show that although most tornadoes rotate counterclockwise, some spin clockwise and develop in a different part of the storm system. This has in turn improved forecasting, because meteorologists now know to look elsewhere for tornadoes. Storm chasers were also the first to determine that tornadoes typically develop in a wall cloud—a low-hanging, slowly rotating cloud about two to six kilometres in diameter that drops down from the main storm cloud.

Simultaneous visual and radar sightings of wall clouds and other thunderstorm features have improved the interpretation of weather radar. This has enabled forecasters to recognize potentially dangerous storms more easily and issue more accurate and timely weather warnings. Moreover, chasers sometimes call in warnings from the field, long before a storm actually develops.

Photographs and videotapes of storms and the structural damage they cause, along with measurements of wind speed and pressure around storm systems, have been used to determine wind speeds around the vortex of a tornado. For example, winds of 150 kilometres an hour can overturn automobiles, and winds of 200 kilometres an hour can drive wood splinters through sheet metal. Winds over 400 kilometres an hour can send concrete blocks and steel beams flying. This information can be used to design safer buildings.

Although the Weather Dogs' aim is to improve forecasting and our understanding of storms, McCarthy says he finds each chase thrilling. "There's so much uncertainty ... You never know what you're going to see," he says. Nonetheless, like most storm chasers with meteorological training, McCarthy esteems the power of nature. And when it comes to safety, his advice is, "If your hair stands on end, run for cover."

The Freakish Effects of Tornadoes in Canada

Tornadoes are the most explosive storms on earth. Their lifting power is evident enough from the feats they accomplish. Tornadoes have plucked the wheels off automobiles. In separate incidents, one tornado raised and turned around a house before setting it neatly back down, and another picked up a locomotive, turned it around in mid-air and set it down on a parallel track facing the opposite way. Tornadoes have stripped asphalt right off the roadway and rolled huge boulders along the ground. And believe it or not, tornadoes have sucked dry small lakes and rivers.

Because the track of a tornado is so narrow—averaging less than 100 metres—it is not uncommon to find buildings on one side of a street obliterated and others on the opposite side left with only a broken window or two, some dents and peeling paint. The combination of awesome destructive power and the narrow damage width has produced the following curious freakish effects:

January 30, 1954

Mid-summer tornadoes occur infrequently in the Maritimes but never in winter. What can only be called a weather freak, a winter tornado struck White Point Beach near Liverpool, N.S. at 11:40 p.m. The winds drove large beams from a newly built barn into the earth to a depth of more than 30 centimetres. The twister also picked up large boulders, used to hold chimney covers in place, and hurled them several metres.

April 16, 1958

A tornado scattered bales of straw across the countryside, south of Watrous, Saskatchewan. The main barn of a pig farmer disappeared, except for the loft floor, which seemed to have fallen after the walls were ripped out, trapping more than 100 pigs. Some were buried in the wreckage, but at least five small pigs were tossed more than two kilometres away.

April 24, 1996

A couple of tornadoes scattered cancelled cheques across south-central Ontario, more than 100 kilometres where they originated. One cheque made out to a butcher shop in Arthur was found by a couple walking to their hayfield outside Orillia. The cancelled cheque belonged to a couple whose farm near Arthur was destroyed by the tornado. As reported in their book, *Under the Whirlwind*, the husband and wife storm chasers Arjen and Jerrine Verkaik describe how the tornado delicately removed the hinge screws from the top of a jewel box before carrying the top 100 metres away, but leaving the bottom of the box in the bathroom window sill. In another weird antic, a crystal vase was left standing upright on the dining room table, but its dozen red roses and water were in the hallway. And while the roof of another building was gone and the bedroom was in shambles, the bed was still neatly made with a pair of slippers still sitting underneath.

May 4, 1964

Following a deadly tornado in New Baltimore, Michigan, at the end of April, debris began showing up in Canada in the Strathroy area of Ontario. Among the found articles were cancelled cheques on the Citizens State Savings Bank, retail sales receipts from a lumber company, a court summons and a boy's sport jacket.

May 24, 1977

A woman in Lafleche, Saskatchewan, was showering when a long piece of two-by-four lumber was driven through the roof and ceiling and came to rest standing upright beside her in the shower—debris dropped by a tornado.

June 5, 1956

In Westlock, Alberta, a bull weighing 635-kilos was resting in his stable, attached to the stall by a logging chain. After the tornado passed, the stall was found 20 metres away with the resident animal stunned but apparently unhurt.

June 7, 1933

In western Ontario, tornadoes have played an assortment of strange pranks. An East Zorra farmer had his ear clipped cleanly off when the wind suddenly slammed the double doors of a barn where he was seeking shelter. A Woodstock man found the linoleum from his kitchen floor in the next door lot, despite the fact that it was weighed down by a heavy stove and half the kitchen furniture. In Kitchener, the wind lifted a garage and carried it 50 metres, dashing it to pieces on railway tracks. It then tore the veranda from another house and carried it to the front lawn of the owner of the wrecked garage, as though in compensation. When the wind ripped the roof off a schoolhouse at Milton, an eleven-year-old girl was driven through a hot-air register in the floor. She suffered only a broken ankle.

June 16, 1923

Tornadic winds snatched a child from the arms of her mother near Ernfold, Saskatchewan. The family was returning to their home from Chaplin, when the tornado swept the girl from their buggy on the outskirts of Uren. In the inky darkness and raging wind and rain-storm, the girl could not be located by her frantic parents. Ten hours later a search party found her asleep in a shack three kilometres from the point where the buggy had been upset.

June 19, 1955

A tornado shattered almost every building at Vita, Manitoba. The storm picked up a cooler full of soft drinks and dropped it into the middle of the main street. Business-minded children decided to sell the drinks for a nickel apiece. A few enterprising students rummaged through the shattered remains of the Vita school to look for questions for the upcoming final examinations, but the teacher was one step ahead of them. He had removed the exams minutes before the storm hit.

June 19, 1978

They called it a miracle in Aubigny, Manitoba. A tornado struck this community's Roman Catholic church and knocked the plaster statue of Saint Antoine, with baby Jesus cradled in its arms, off the top of the steeple. The steeple was in ruins, but the statue came to rest on the front lawn of the church without a scratch, staring serenely toward the northeast, as though noting the track of the tornado. One town resident lost her freezer, which ended up in the basement of another house but without the meat. Said another resident, "The last time I saw our bathroom [outhouse], it was going down the street as fast as you please." Though not a drop of rain fell during the storm, the southern and western sides of most houses and outbuildings were blackened and impregnated with muddy groundwater sucked up by the twister.

June 23, 1910
A Lumsden, Saskatchewan, fellow lost his trousers and later, to his surprise, found them swinging from a tree two kilometres away.

June 26, 1870
Near Belleville, a severe thunderstorm and tornado spread millions of tiny toads, each about the size of "a 3-cent piece," across the ground for several kilometres. Local residents said that the same phenomenon occurred on four other occasions.

June 30, 1912
In the Regina "cyclone," tornadic winds lifted canoeists from Wascana Lake and deposited them one to two kilometres away, with paddles still in place; one person was dashed into a brick wall and killed; and another was set down in trees, dazed and covered with mud and garbage but still alive. That same tornado carried telephone poles vertically down the street.

July 1, 1772
The earliest known tornado to strike Canada levelled a tract of forest in the Niagara Peninsula area of Ontario. In those days, building roads was long and arduous work, but this storm made the task easier by clearing a perfectly clean and straight path through the trees. The road became known as Hurricane Road.

July 1, 1909

A tornado at Springside, Saskatchewan, tore all the shingles off one side of the school, raced across the road, took the roof off a barn, recrossed the road and lifted a horse about 12 metres in the air, took him some distance and dropped him unharmed. The storm also carried away a smokehouse full of meat.

July 1, 1985

A 26-year-old man was killed when he tangled with a mini-tornado while para-sailing on a lake near Turner Valley, Alberta. The victim was wearing a special para-sail, similar to a regular parachute, and was being pulled behind a boat just above the surface of the water. Although the winds were calm at the time, a whirlwind no wider than 15 metres suddenly appeared from the west and enveloped the man. He didn't see it coming until it hit. The whirlwind lifted the man about 60 metres into the air, snapping his 90-metre-long nylon tow rope and then dropped him in a field a half kilometre east of the lake, where he struck a barbed-wire fence before landing. He died on impact.

July 5, 1970

A tornado tore the roof off a barn south of Verigin, Saskatchewan. That same barn had its roof lifted off by tornadic winds on two other occasions over 25 years.

July 15, 1946

A cow in Sedley, Saskatchewan, was found lying on her back, four legs in the air, and anchored to the ground by her horns after a tornado struck. The farmer chose not to milk the cow because he thought it would be sour.

July 18, 1991

Small tornadoes and downburst winds in northwestern Ontario flattened up to 30 million trees in less than an hour, the worst such forest blowdown in Canadian forestry history.

July 22, 1920

In an area of southeastern Saskatchewan well known for its severe summer weather, the worst tornado ever to strike the area touched down between Yellow Grass and Alameda. On one farm, a buggy went over the top of the house. The wind hoisted a hired man and blew him unharmed into the middle of a field. Elsewhere, 16 horses were completely stripped of their hair and a 800-kilo stallion was air-lifted for almost a kilometre. He was found uninjured, with a piece of manger still attached to his halter. At another farm, the twister threw a woman, sick with flu, from her bed into the yard, demolishing the house in the act. All the furnishings and family belongings disappeared in the storm. Just 15 minutes before the storm destroyed the local schoolhouse, the teacher had allowed the students to leave. Schoolbooks and papers were later found as far away as 45 kilometres.

July 24, 1965

A tornado felled trees, damaged homes, levelled crops and left fish swimming in a storm-created pond on the main street of Erieau, Ontario. It is thought that the waterspout sucked the blue gills from a pond at the north edge of town.

July 31, 1987

One of the more bizarre events in the Edmonton tornado tragedy was that a week-old baby was found bundled in a blanket at the peak of the mayhem on a road. No one knew who the infant was, and she lay in intensive care until late that night, when her grandfather ended a frantic family search by identifying the child at the hospital.

August 1, 1935

After a tornado took the roof off a cheese factory near Cornwall, Ontario, winds lifted the roof from a railway station and set it on the roofless factory. A 400-kilo gasoline engine flew nearly a kilometre and buried itself in the ground. A piano and an organ were part of the furnishings of a house razed by the tornado. A single ivory key was found a kilometre away.

August 3, 1916

A tornado levelled crops and destroyed several large barns near Wynyard, Saskatchewan. One farmer tending to his horses was caught under the barn when a huge beam fell on his chest. Near him lay the horses. Neighbours rescued the farmer, but the local doctor pronounced him dead. His obituary appeared in the next issue of the local newspaper. However, 13 hours later he regained consciousness, and although it took him a long time to recuperate, he lived to be almost 80.

August 7, 1979

Following the deadly Woodstock tornado, a live pig was found stuck in a fork of a tree, where the wind had carried it. One of the local paper carriers phoned to ask the newspaper staff if he still had to deliver his route where all the houses had disappeared.

August 11, 1980

A mini-tornado struck a hamburger stand on the beach at Port Dover, Ontario. The strong wind stood a bench on end. Tops popped off vinegar dispensers. Several ice cream cones were slammed into a nearby chain-link fence. Grease from a deep fryer flew out and splattered the walls and floor of the stand. Within minutes of the storm, a customer, unaware of what had just happened, walked in and ordered some fries.

August 14, 1989

A small building in Carlisle, N.B., disappeared completely during a tornado, but the dozen storm windows stored inside the building were virtually untouched, with only 2 of the 24 panes of glass broken.

August 15, 1997

A tornado ripped through a cottage southeast of Owen Sound, Ontario, hurling two men 100 metres out into a lake. The force of the wind held the two underwater and spun them around in a whirlpool. Miraculously, though bleeding and bruised, they fought their way safely to shore through a floating tangle of torn-up trees, building debris and furniture.

August 17, 1958

A mini-tornado roared out of a forest fire in the Douglas Lake range-lands of British Columbia, enveloping two firefighters in flames. The twister hurled them into the air like flaming torches, burning 75 per-cent of their bodies. The men later died from their burns. (These small whirlwinds are like dust devils and are generated by the enor-mous heat of a forest fire.)

August 30, 1947

The tornado that roared through Gooderham, Ontario, and two nearby counties blew five people 100 metres from a wrecked house into the tops of a clump of cedar trees. Screaming in terror, bleeding and naked, they clung to the branches for dear life. Throughout the countryside, the tornado also played fantastic pranks, uprooting trees and telephone poles and planting them firmly upside down in the earth. Near Coe Hill, the storm lifted a service station off its foun-dation, sucked out a car inside and parked it on top of the structure with sufficient force to crush the roof. One house was flattened, and not one stick of furniture remained. Yet, in the cellar were preserves on the shelves, ready to be opened for supper.

September 10, 1942

A tornado dug up a farmer's potato crop north of Killarney, Manitoba. The twister tore the clothes off several children and pulled a woman out a window. About thirty years earlier, a tornado had pulled sod off a tenth of a hectare, leaving it as bare as a floor.

STORM BREWING?
THE NOSE KNOWS

Lauchie McDougall of Wreckhouse, Newfoundland, had such a keen nose for the weather that he was actually paid to smell approaching storms. McDougall was a part-time cattle farmer and trapper, but it was his job as "gale sniffer extraordinaire" that made him a Newfoundland legend.

Wreckhouse is located on a barren stretch of the Trans-Canada Highway in southwest Newfoundland, about 20 kilometres from Port aux Basques. It is an area known for its high winds, with gales as strong as 140 kilometres per hour gaining strength as they sweep down from Table Mountain across the highway and out to sea. Wreckhouse winds are notorious for lifting freight cars off their tracks and blowing over tractor trailers.

The word ozone derives from the Greek for "smell," because of the characteristic odour it gives off when sparked during an electrical discharge. Had a whiff of ozone? Smell that pungent clean odour after a thunderstorm or the "electric" smell of a subway train, and you've smelled ozone gas.

Thus the Newfoundland Railway Company and later the Canadian National Railways contracted McDougall to report on the winds for a salary reported to be a maximum of $140 annually. Three or four times a day for 30 years, until his death in 1965, McDougall would sniff out gusts of wind down by the railway tracks and warn officials in Port aux Basques if he sensed super winds brewing. All nearby trains would then be kept outside the danger area or chained to their tracks until the winds abated. Whatever McDougall said was regarded with great trust. One railroader recalls, "Many's the train had to stop because Lauchie said so." Once, when officials failed to heed his warning, 22 cars were blown off the tracks.

Following his death, McDougall's wife, Emily, continued to sniff out winds from Table Mountain until she retired in 1973. In 1982, the CN erected a plaque in the terminal building in Port aux Basques, com-

During certain meteorological conditions, the winds in southwestern Newfoundland between Port aux Basques and St. Andrews sometimes reach strengths that can blow transport trucks off the highway and trains off the tracks. Meteorologists at the Maritime Weather Centre know them as a mountain lee wave effect, but refer to them in wind warnings as "Wreckhouse Winds."

memorating the work of the McDougalls—who surely had one of the oddest professions anywhere.

We have all met people whose sensitive noses are able to smell an approaching storm or rain coming. Although he's no Lauchie McDougall, Keith Fraser, a geographer, says that he can always smell rain outside his west Ottawa home before the first drops reach the ground. With an easterly wind, he smells the sour odours from the E. B. Eddy Pulp Mill across the river in Hull. In Ottawa, nearly half of all easterly winds bear rain or snow, whereas only 12 percent of all other winds bring any type of precipitation. There's some weather lore that seems especially appropriate in the nation's capital: *When the wind is in the east, 'tis good for neither man nor beast.*

In his delightful *British Columbia Weather Book*, the B.C. weatherman Phil Reimer says that when you can smell the MacMillan-Bloedel Harmac pulp mill south of Nanaimo, it's going to rain. Again, foul weather tends to ride on easterly winds.

Animals sometimes seem to have far greater sensitivity to approaching weather than humans do. Farmers swear you can count on a rainstorm coming if cows huddle together or lie down in a pasture, or if horses stand with their tails to the wind or roll over. An old saying says, When sheep collect and huddle, tomorrow will become a puddle. And pigs are said to be especially sensitive, moving sticks and straw before any rain, and squealing at the first signs of a change in the weather. Virgil, the Roman poet, wrote of pigs "tossing their snouts" when a storm was near.

Long before weather forecasters talked of isobars and kilopascals, shepherds, sailors and settlers developed theories about the smell of rain. It was said that flowers smell sweeter just before a rainstorm and tobacco pipes and manure piles stronger. One old-time rhyme says, When the ditch and pond offend the nose, then look out for rain and stormy blows.

And sure enough, the decay of organic debris in stagnant ponds, drains, gutters and ditches produces methane and other gases that accumulate in pockets and bubbles under the mud. These gases and their odours are suppressed under high pressure, but when low-pressure systems (usually associated with stormy weather) approach, the bubbles of putrid gas expand, rise to the surface and break loose in sufficient quantities to give the local atmosphere an offensive smell. The same lowering of pressure may be marked by the rising of water in wells or toilet bowls, or by more foam on rivers.

Aristotle noted more than 2,000 years ago that shepherds believed that rain became sweetly scented from its passage through the heavens, and that even rainbows had an aroma. Yet we cannot really smell rain because water has no odour. Some meteorologists attribute the smell of thunderstorms to the pungency of ozone; lightning can split apart air molecules, which recombine to form ozone, leaving a sharp but short-lived odour. But several possibilities exist as to why human beings can smell rain coming.

"I believe the behaviour of scent depends on two things—the condition of the ground and the temperature of the air—both of which I apprehend should be moist, without being wet. When both are in this condition, the scent is then perfect and vice versa, when the ground is hard and the air dry, there seldom will be any scent."—Peter Beckford in *Thoughts on Hunting* **(18th century).**

It could be all in the nose. Higher humidity, such as is usually associated with rain, sharpens our sense of smell, and everything smells stronger when it gets damp. As the moisture content of the air increases just prior to rain, the aromatic molecules of many substances become covered with a layer of water molecules. And these larger, hydrated molecules cling more easily to the mucous surfaces inside the nose.

The hydration of aromatic molecules may explain why animals and insects communicate through scents. Masters of fox hunts claim that

156 Weather Observing and Forecasting

hunting scents depend mostly on the water content of the ground and air, both of which should be moist without being wet. When the ground is hard and the air is dry, there is seldom any trail for the hounds to follow, but rising humidity improves the line of scent.

Test for yourself the effect of humidity on odour. After taking a shower, compare how strong a perfume smells in the misty bathroom with how it smelled before turning on the water.

Many botanists believe that the smell associated with rain on land originates with volatile substances given off by vegetation—terpenes from pine forests, for instance, or creosote from desert bushes and various organic smells from meadows. (This, surely, is what sometimes enables mariners to follow their noses through fog—the difference between the heavy salt smell of a sea breeze and a sweet garden smell from a land breeze.) Scientists estimate that plants and trees exude some 450 million tonnes of plant volatiles, predominantly terpenes, in the atmosphere each year, mainly during the summer months. Apparently, when relative humidity is high or the plant is wet, plant stomata enlarge, and this leads to an increase in the escape of these substances into the atmosphere.

In the 1960s, Australian chemists found that certain types of clays exude a strong "rain" smell when relative humidity exceeded 80 percent. They found that the smell comes from a yellowish oil trapped in rocks and soil, called petrichor—derived from the Greek words *petros*, "stone," and *khor*, the ethereal fluid that flowed like blood in the veins of the gods. Petrichor is commonly observed as the pleasant, refreshing, earthy odour that frequently accompanies the first rains after a warm dry period.

Petrichor comes from atmospheric haze, which contains the terpenes, creosotes and other volatile compounds that emanate from plants. In the air, these substances undergo oxidation and nitration before being absorbed in the soil or trapped in rocks. Absorption is usually highest when relative humidity is at its lowest. But when the relative humidity climbs above 80 percent, the moisture in the air begins to fill the pores of the rock and the spaces in dry clays with water, displacing the odorous and volatile compounds that then enter the air. Because

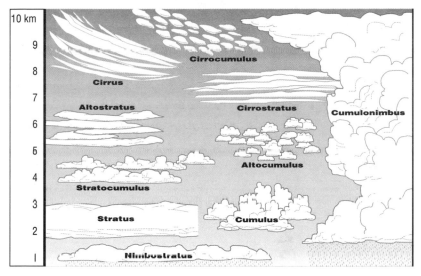

By noting the different shapes and textures of clouds, you can do a reasonable job of forecasting the weather.

the earthy scent is so often followed by rain, we learn to associate the two.

Smelling rain, seeing a distant thundercloud and feeling dampness in the air may not by themselves mean rain, but when combined with hearing a weather forecast, they are almost a sure sign of rain within an hour.

BE YOUR OWN
WEATHERPERSON

During the first half of this century, professional rainmakers (called professors) would travel across the Great Plains of North America selling rainmaking in drought-stricken areas. They often unveiled a weather machine called a *universcope* that spouted coloured smoke upward into the sky. Of course, the rain professors would read the sky and then stoke the machines only when there was a good chance of rain. These early cloud seeders knew that for their weather prophecies to have any chance of success, they had to be able to read the sky, assess the current weath-

The highest clouds in the atmosphere are called noctilucent, or luminous night clouds. These thin streaky clouds are very rare, found at heights above 80 kilometres, where the temperature is consistently between -75°C and -90°C and where water vapour is non-existent. Generally, noctilucent clouds can only be seen at twilight when sunlight reflects off ice crystals or ice-covered dust that lies at the outer limits of the earth's atmosphere, and usually only in late summer. The best place in the world to see noctilucent clouds is Canada.

er and guess how it would behave over the next couple of hours, which for their business was long enough. A professor with a good weather eye and good luck would soon develop a good reputation.

The former Boston television news reporter Jack Borden is a kind of modern-day rainmaker, peddling clouds instead of rain. Borden is founder of For Spacious Skies, a non-profit educational organization dedicated to increasing sky awareness in people's lives.

More than 20 years ago, on one delightful June day in Boston, with the sky a rich blue and speckled with fluffy white clouds, Jack Borden conducted a series of person-on-the-street interviews for the evening news, requesting that interviewees "without looking up, describe the sky." To his astonishment, none could.

That experience changed Borden into a self-described "Johnny Appleseed of the Sky." Borden contends that except for spectacular events like sunsets, halos and lightning storms, most people never see the sky. "We breathe the sky an average of sixteen times a minute, but most of us are unaware of its beauty, majesty, power and fragility." With the conviction of a crusading evangelist, Borden wants us to receive the sky into our lives. Across America, he has brought the sky into classrooms and Sunday schools, nursing homes, prisons, mental hospitals and rehab centres, introducing people to the beauty above and the world around by simply encouraging them to look up.

Weather should be important to us, beyond the obvious reasons of knowing what to wear or when to mow the lawn. Being weatherwise can help to protect our property from damage and prevent us from becoming weather statistics. Further, because weather knows no borders, it teaches the lesson how interconnected we are with one another. Weather is also a chance for young people to develop sensitivity to what's really going on around them.

Watching the sky and its contents can be inspirational, comforting and soothing. Guessing how it will change over the next little while can be great fun. Furthermore, it requires no special equipment or transportation. It's free! And it all begins by looking up.

A century or more ago, skying was a daily activity. Everyone had to be a weatherperson. Outdoors people—shipmates, trappers and farmhands—people whose lives and livelihoods depended on coming storms, thickness of the fog, breakup of river and lake ice and maturing of the crop—were seasoned weather forecasters, judging for themselves present and approaching weather.

It used to be that reading the sky and watching the clouds was a valuable skill handed down through generations. Now that skill is all but extinct. Regrettably, nowadays most people take weather for granted. Few of us take time to lie down on the grass to see shapes in clouds or watch the ever-changing colour of the sky. It's so much a backdrop for daily events that we habituate ourselves to it—like Musak, Borden says. Instead of going outside and gazing at the western sky, sticking a wet finger into the wind, sniffing for rain or feeling the dampness in the air, we are more likely to turn on The Weather Network, tune in to Weatheradio, log on to www.weather.com or simply ask someone else.

Bob Dylan was right when he said, "You don't need to be a weatherman to know which way the wind blows." Through careful observation and study, people can often make their own forecasts for the next few hours.

All prophecies, though, must begin with skywatching. By noting the shape and texture of clouds, the colour of the sky, wind speed and direction and temperature and moisture changes, you can do a reasonable job of predicting coming storms, morning frost or dew and evening calms. Instead of relying on television broadcasters alone, step outside and expose all your senses to the atmosphere.

Over time, it is possible to develop a few basic forecasting rules that you can use to adapt the official, regional forecast to suit your local situation or circumstances. Here's a handy list of practical weather signs that can hint at the weather ahead. They are generally applicable to most locations in Canada, year-round, although the amateur forecaster would want to adapt the guidelines in accordance with local controls such as the moderation of water bodies, changes in terrain and landscape and urban/rural effects.

Look for cloudy, unsettled weather when:

- The barometer falls steadily
- The wind blows strongly in the early morning
- The temperature at night is higher than usual (sky is cloudy)
- The temperature is far above or below normal for the time of year
- Clouds rapidly move in various directions at different levels
- High, thin, wispy clouds (cirrus) increase in amount, thicken and lower, sometimes producing a ring or halo around the sun or moon
- Clouds darken on a summer afternoon
- High- and/or middle-level clouds darken and move from the south and southwest
- The sunrise is red

Look for steady rain or snow when:

- The barometer falls steadily (if the pressure falls slowly, rain or snow will come within a day; if it falls rapidly, expect precipitation any minute)
- Winds blow from the southeast to northeast and north
- Clouds are low and uniformly flat and grey
- Leaves show their undersides, as strong south wind in advance of the rain will flip the leaves over
- There is a ring around the sun or moon

Look for more pleasant weather when:

- The barometer is steady or rising slowly
- A gentle breeze blows steadily from the west to northwest
- Winds swing from south to southwest, or from east or northeast to the northwest

- The amount of cloud cover and the number of clouds decrease in the late afternoon
- The cloud base rises and humidity decreases
- The evening sky is clear and you can look directly at the setting sun, which resembles a ball of fire
- Morning fog breaks within two hours of sunrise
- The night before heavy dew or frost occurs
- The moon shines brightly and the wind is light
- There is a bright blue sky with high thin wisps of cloud

Look for clearing skies when:
- The barometer rises
- The wind shifts to any westerly direction (especially from east through south to the west)
- The temperature falls rapidly, especially in the afternoon
- Increasing breaks occur in the overcast
- Clouds become lumpy
- Dark clouds become lighter and steadily rise in altitude
- Fog lifts before noon
- Frost or dew is on the grass

Look for showers (thundershowers) when:
- The barometer falls
- Winds blow from the south or southeast
- The morning temperature is unusually high, air is moist and sticky and you see cumulus clouds building (rain within six hours)
- Dark, threatening thunderclouds develop in a westerly wind
- Thick, fluffy clouds (cumulus) develop rapidly upward during early afternoon
- You hear loud static on your AM radio (thunderstorms within the hour)

Look for heavy snow when:
- The air temperature is between $-10°C$ and $-1°C$
- The barometer falls rapidly

Studies show that crickets chirp faster when it's warm than when it's cold. If you count the number of cricket chirps in eight seconds, then add four, 9 times out of 10, you'll have the temperature to within one degree Celsius. The technique, however, doesn't work well in January.

- Winds blow from the east or northeast
- A storm lies to the south and east of you

Look for temperatures to rise when:
- The wind shifts from the north or west to the south
- The nighttime sky is overcast with a moderate southerly wind
- The sky is clear all day
- The barometer falls steadily (in winter)

Look for temperatures to fall when:
- The barometer rises steadily (in winter)
- The wind shifts into the north or northwest from the south
- The wind is light and the sky is clear at night
- Skies are clearing, especially in the winter
- Snowflurries occur with a west or north wind

Look for fog when:
- Warm winds are blowing humid air across a much colder surface (either land or sea)
- The sky is clear, the winds are light and the air is humid the night before
- Warm rain is falling ahead of the warm air
- Water temperatures are warm and the air is much colder

A final word on weather predictions: one indicator makes lucky your guess, two indicators make errors much less; so take the weather sign at its word if you look again and see a third.

Keeping Your Own Weather Records

Weather observers with Environment Canada make a daily record of weather conditions in their locales at the same time each day. You can learn a great deal about weather and confirm the day's forecast by keeping a weather diary.

At regular times each day, fill in observations of weather, cloud type and other sky observations. Note the wind direction and estimate its speed using the Beaufort wind scale (an explanation of which appears on page 169). Include a mention of how the weather changed from day to day or from night to day. Make space for personal observations of interesting weather events such as hail, fog, heavy snow, thunderstorms, strong winds, ice pellets and heavy frost. Instrument recordings of temperature and precipitation at nearby stations can be taken from the local newspaper or television reports.

Make note of the occurrence of other non-regular events such as snow shovelling and grass mowing and annually recurring events in nature such as the dates of the flowering of lilacs, first sightings of robins or other migrating birds, the emergence of insects or the impact of the first frost in your garden or flowerbeds.

When you supplement their observations with a regular look at the weather map published in most daily newspapers or seen on local television weathercasts, you'll get a closer sense of how weather works.

Weatherlore—Fact or Fiction?

Long before meteorologists discovered cold fronts and jet streams, people relied on nature to foretell the next day's weather. Farmers, mariners and hunters showed a keen sense of observation and quickly connected changes in the environment with rhythms or patterns of weather. They recalled what they saw in the form of short sayings, often embodied in rhyme for ease of remembering.

Most weather folklore is a kind of whimsical silliness, imaginative and often contradictory, far-fetched and unfounded, useless and superstitious and quite harmless, though loads of fun. Many meteorologists scoff at weather superstitions. However, many folk sayings have stood the test of scientific scrutiny, even though they were developed without instruments or knowledge about the causes of weather. Those that have a chance of success are ones that prophesy daily weather changes. Most useful weatherlore relates the coming weather to one weather sign, such as the character and movement of clouds, the colour and appearance of the sky or the direction and strength of the wind, but weather is so complex that relying on one element alone is by no means a sure thing.

I have always found separating wisdom from superstition in weather folklore great fun! Here are some of my favourite weather sayings; some are about as silly as it gets, and others should be believed:

Dew on the grass, rain won't come to pass.

Evening red and morning grey, two sure signs of one fine day.

The sudden storm lasts not three hours
The sharper the blast, the sooner 'tis past.

The higher the clouds, the better the weather.

Cold is the night when the stars shine bright.

Sound travelling far and wide a stormy day betide.

When the ditch and pond offend the nose,
Then look out for rain and stormy blows.

Rain long foretold, long last,
Short notice, soon will pass.

If bees stay at home, rain will soon come.
If they fly away, fine will be the day.

A rainbow afternoon,
Good weather coming soon.

Catchy drawer and sticky door,
Coming rain will pour and pour.

The winds of the daytime wrestle and fight,
Longer and stronger than those of the night.

When down the chimney falls the soot
Mud will soon be underfoot.

When the chairs squeak, it's of rain they speak.

The squeak of the snow will the temperature show.

By watching the sky, noting down your observations and study-ing daily weather maps, you'll soon gain additional insight into how the weather develops locally:

Here are three examples:

- When the overnight temperature is fore-cast to fall close to freezing, local condi-tions determine whether a killing frost will develop.

Expect morning frost when the sky the night before is clear, the winds are light and the air is humid. The killing frost may not materialize if a protective mantle of clouds forms or a stirring breeze starts blowing during the night.

- When dew, frost or fog appear on the grass in the early morning, there is a good chance the day will be fair and bright.

On clear, cool, calm nights, ground moisture in the form of frost, dew or fog may form more readily because clouds are not present to interfere with ground cooling. Calm, clear nights are typical of high-pressure weather conditions, and fine weather is likely to continue for at least the next day. Cloud cover keeps the earth from losing heat; therefore, the temperature near the

Clouds travel thousands of kilo-metres horizontal-ly but no more than 18 kilo-metres vertically. They cover half the world's sky at any one time, but account for a minute amount of the earth's mois-ture; squeeze it all out and you'll get a depth of less than three centi-metres of water to cover the planet.

earth's surface cannot cool off enough to condense the moisture in the air and form dew or frost.

- When you can smell odours from a ditch or pond more readily, rain and strong winds are coming.

The air surrounding a centre of low pressure, such as a storm, is forced upward with decreasing pressure. This phenomenon is analogous to taking the lid off a coffee pot, where odours held in place by sinking air around high pressure are suddenly released. Accordingly, odours become stronger, whether from a bed of roses or from a pond, particularly when aided by higher humidity.

The Importance of Clouds

Today's clouds announce tomorrow's weather. By becoming familiar with various forms of cloud and their movement, you'll also be able to make good guesses about approaching weather.

Generally speaking, clouds moving from the south herald precipitation, and those from the north signify clear weather. Also useful to know is that the higher the clouds, the finer the weather. This stems from the fact that high, thin cirrus clouds are not generally associated with precipitation. However, they are often precursors, and depending on the situation, precipitation can quickly follow.

Some additional weather tips from clouds:

- The more cloud types present, the greater the chance of rain or snow
- Clouds during the day can often lower the high temperatures; at night they will often trap heat, making for warmer minimum temperatures
- Higher cloud layers move with prevailing winds aloft that carry weather systems; lower clouds reflect local influences

The three main types of clouds to recognize are high level, middle level and low level. Characteristics of 10 major cloud types include:

High Cloud—(above 6,000 to 8,000 metres)

1. *Cirrus.* Thin, wispy small white clouds that often occur as feathery filaments or long streamers resembling jet contrails stretching across the sky. Often their ends are swept by strong winds, giving them the look of a horse's tail. Cirrus clouds are fair-weather clouds. If they thicken or spread out into sheets across most of the sky, expect rain or snow within 48 hours. If cirrus do not thicken, fair weather usually continues.

2. *Cirrostratus.* Milky white uniform veil of thin, transparent cloud, comprising ice crystals. Sometimes accompanied by a halo around the sun or moon, which usually means wet weather within 12 hours.

3. *Cirrocumulus.* Thin bands of either continuous or patchy small clouds, white or pale grey in colour. A ripple or rib pattern gives them a look of fish scales, referred to as a *mackerel sky.* They signal a change to heavier cloud cover usually within a day. When they are followed by lower and thicker clouds, look for rain and warmer temperature.

A sudden rise in wind speed may foretell a change in the weather. Likewise, a quick shift in wind direction indicates a turn in the weather. On the whole, winds from the east and south are foul-weather winds; northerly and westerly winds are fair-weather winds. That's why common wisdom says that "it's best to do business when the wind is in the northwest."

Middle Clouds—(between 2,500 and 6,000 metres)

4. *Altocumulus.* Either patchy or continuous middle cumulus cloud with a dappled or rippled appearance, often with a flat bottom. They are considered a thicker and lower version of cirrocumulus. Altocumulus clouds are reliable indicators of changeable weather and an impending storm.

5. *Altostratus.* Pale grey, uniform layer of cloud that is much thicker and lower than cirrostratus. Although they are too thick and low for halos to be formed, the sun can still be seen weakly through the overcast. Usually a reliable sign of precipitation within a few hours.

6. *Stratocumulus.* Low layers of grey or whitish clouds with occasional dark patches that have a well-defined rounded or undulating appearance. Stratocumulus may have a few breaks, but usually cloud cover extends for hundreds of kilometres. They signal changing weather, often preceding a cold front and possible thunderstorm.

Low Cloud—(below 2,500 metres)

7. *Stratus.* A uniformly grey, opaque blanket of cloud that may be continuous or patchy, often producing light drizzle or flurries. Its low base often obscures hilltops and tall buildings. Without much texture, it looks like high drifting fog, making for a dull, grey day. At the earth's surface, stratus is simply fog. Fair weather usually follows the disappearance of stratus.

8. *Nimbostratus.* A dark, thick, monotonous deck of low cloud providing continuous rain or snow. Usually covers the entire sky, hiding the sun. May mean days of steady rain.

9. *Cumulus.* Puffy, white, heaped or piled clouds that often form by day, disappear by night and re-form the next day. The flat, well-defined base begins around 600 metres up in winter and 1,200 metres in summer. Cumulus clouds are associated with fair weather, blue sky and no precipitation.

Vertical Cloud

10. *Cumulonimbus.* Mammoth cumulus clouds with a dark base and a smooth anvil-shaped top. Called the kings of the sky, they are the biggest of all clouds, often towering in excess of 12 kilometres. CBs are storm clouds associated with severe thunderstorms, heavy rain and sometimes hail or tornadoes.

The Beaufort Wind Scale

Sir Francis Beaufort of the British Royal Navy devised the wind-wave scale in 1805. It originally referred to the amount of sail a full-rigged ship could carry in specific wind conditions. In light wind, just one sail would be taken in; in a heavy storm the number would be 11, therefore Beaufort force 11.

The Beaufort scale has been modified several times. Basically, the idea is to estimate wind speed by watching the *effects* of wind on such things as flags, trees, smoke, water surface and even people.

Beaufort Wind Force	Wind Speed (km/h)	Wind Type	Descriptive Effects
0	below 1	calm	smoke rises vertically
1	2–5	light air	smoke drifts slowly
2	6–11	slight breeze	leaves rustle; wind vanes move; wind felt on faces
3	12–19	gentle breeze	leaves and twigs in constant motion; wind extends light flag
4	20–29	moderate breeze	small branches move; raises dust and loose paper
5	30–38	fresh breeze	small trees sway
6	39–50	strong breeze	large branches in continuous motion; utility wires whistle
7	51 61	near gale	whole trees in motion; wind affects walking
8	62–74	fresh gale	twigs and small branches break off trees
9	75–87	strong gale	branches break; shingles blow from roofs
10	88–101	storm	trees snap and uproot; some damage to buildings
11	102–117	violent storm	property damage widespread
12	118–	hurricane	severe and extensive damage

Weather— More than Tomorrow's Forecast

A tornado touches down in Saint Stanislas, Quebec. *Stephene Dupont/Canapress.*

WHEN IN DOUBT, BLAME IT ON THE WEATHER

Near three o'clock one morning in January 1988, some 200 Department of National Defence air-raid sirens blared for about 45 minutes in southern Ontario. Later that year, an Ontario District County Court judge refused to sentence a man even though a jury had found him guilty on two counts of assault. In late January 1994, the City of Toronto had a shortfall of $2.5 million because its parking enforcement officers in Toronto were 100,000 tickets below their monthly quota.

What do these seemingly unrelated events have in common? The weather! In the first case, high winds and freezing rain had apparently set off the alarms. In the second incident, the judge claimed that a heat wave made the courtroom so hot, humid and uncomfortable that the accused was "deprived of his constitutional right to a fair trial." And in the final case, the coldest Toronto January in 70 years froze fingers and clogged pens—but instead of using pencils, officials blamed the weather.

The most imaginative use of the weather excuse has to go to the chairman of a South African company manufacturing cat litter. Explaining the lower profits from his company's business, the CEO blamed "the extremely dry summer, which meant cats spent more of their time outside."

What a convenient excuse the weather is— sometimes legitimately—for events gone awry, for our ailments or for bailing us out of commitments. "It's too hot," "it's too cold" or "we can't do that because a storm's coming" are about the handiest excuses we'll ever have. It's no longer "the devil made me do it," or "there's something in the water." Rather, we blame El Niño and ozone holes.

Why is weather our favourite excuse? Because no other factor, except perhaps health, looms larger in our daily lives and so directly affects our actions. Weather affects what we eat, how we feel and how we behave. Weather also plays a large part in influencing market supply and demand: it can create inflation, financial crisis and social unrest. It has enormous economic consequence on activities like farming, recreation, energy and transportation. It provides 365 different excuses each year for what goes wrong or can't be explained. David Taylor, chief climatologist for Weather Services Corporation, a Massachusetts firm that supplies weather forecasts for businesses around the world, claims that "some companies hire us because they can blame us." That's why weather blaming is as familiar in Calgary as it is in Calcutta. It is still conversation's first topic, running well ahead of politics, relatives and sports.

Some of the hottest weather in St. Petersburg, Russia, this century occurred during the summer of 1995. Valdimir Zhirinovsky, the ultra-nationalist leader, blamed the heat on the West. He called on all true patriots to resist this meteorological aggression.

Weather has great appeal as a scapegoat because it is impersonal, random, complex and uncontrollable. Nothing can be done about it. No guilt—it's nature's fault! Why do airlines so often use weather as a reason for flight delays? Because no one blames the airlines—passengers just curse the weather 500 kilometres away.

Unlike worn excuses such as traffic and family or the dog ate my homework, blaming the weather goes unchallenged. Instead, it invites similar, or better yet, more horrible life experiences from our listeners: black ice, frozen pipes and baseball-sized hail. For those who demand scapegoats for the weather, it's left to nations, or groups of people. Americans blame Canadians for cold weather and Canadians blame Siberians. For years, any weird, wild or woolly weather we blamed on the Russians. The end of the Cold War has ended those excuses. Even cold-loving Russians are saying that the winters were better under the Communists. In winter 1992–93, a lengthy mild spell and rare winter thunderstorms brought slush on roads and sidewalks.

Of course, there is often good reason to blame the weather. Every day it causes misery, hardship and misfortune somewhere in the world. According to the United Nations, from 1967 to 1992 weather-related

A warm, dry foehn wind, called the chinook in southern Alberta and the Santa Ana in California, has been linked with an increase in psychiatric disorders and mental-hospital admissions. People's reaction time is slowed down, and they are more irritable and lethargic. However, some people are energized by the wind. In southern Alberta, researchers have attempted to explain the apparent high divorce and suicide rates on the occurrence of chinooks. Said one resident of Medicine Hat, "I always know when the chinook wind blows—our church choir sings off-key."

events killed about 3.5 million people and further affected 2.8 billion. Economic losses from these disasters in 1992 alone amounted to $90 billion.

Too often, however, weather gets blamed when closer inspection reveals that the problem lies elsewhere. In January 1995, mild weather in central Ontario left usually safe lakes and rivers with huge patches of open water or thin ice that could not support snowmobiles. So weather was said to be the cause of a record number of deaths. But don't the snowmobilers bear some responsibility? Some people exploit weather as a reason to do something unpopular—like raising coffee prices 50 percent when frost kills 10 percent of the Brazilian coffee beans. Others use it as the perfect substitute for unknown causes; they suggest, for instance, that weather caused a rash of robberies in certain neighbourhoods or falling revenues at gambling casinos. Weather is the best "educated guess" excuse! And it certainly beats human failure, especially our own. In early 1996, several restaurants blamed a spate of nasty snowstorms that struck just before dinner on several Saturdays for keeping people at home. Those same storms also apparently kept people from dieting. Weight Watchers saw attendance drop 20 percent at their meetings in January and February, normally the prime diet season.

Fascinated by the frequency and scope of weather excuses in our society, I began several years ago to collect anecdotes from newspapers and magazines. Below is a sampling, ranging from the mundane to the astonishing.

Athletes are among those most skilled at picking on the weather. The "boys of summer" often credit unseasonably cold Aprils for stiff joints, batting slumps and poor starts. Even coaches say that the short Canadian playing season leaves too little time for adequate development of baseball players. However, the weather in Canada is no worse than in places like Massachusetts or Michigan, and they produce a lot of ballplayers. In 1991, Indy 500 drivers blamed crashes on cold tires due to unseasonably cold weather. In 1994, Canadian bobsledders said humidity on their runners resulted in their poor performance at the winter Olympics in Lillehammer. And in March 1995, curlers at the Brier in Halifax complained almost as much about the weather outside as they did about the frost on the ice inside.

Unseasonable weather is blamed repeatedly for economic woes. In my collection, weather was singled out, time and time again, as the sole reason for a rise in unemployment, a jump in the consumer price index, more bankruptcies, a decline in housing starts, dwindling profits, earnings disclaimers, rising costs and a drop in the balance of payments. Has the weather report become the latest economic indicator?

When retailers need a reason for a downturn, weather is their favourite scapegoat, and it may be a good reason when it comes to goods such as bathing suits, skis and air conditioners. An early snowstorm does wonders for selling winter boots and coats. But is it realistic to attribute to the weather all major slowdowns in sales without considering sticker shock, recession, overexpansion or competition?

Men and women suffer through the same number of colds annually— 2.2—but women feel more miserable, according to a study by the pharmaceutical manufacturer Smith/Kline Beecham. In a poll of 150 men and 150 women, the firm found that women more often blame external causes such as the weather or being around infected people for colds. Men are more likely to blame themselves for not getting enough rest, vitamins or exercise. For home remedies, women choose juice; men opt for a hot toddy.

In general, industrial, business and financial managers largely ignore weather when making economic decisions. However, they are quick to use it as an excuse when things go wrong. In my collection, breweries blamed flat beer sales on cool wet summer weather; snowblower manufacturers blamed near-snowless winters on their losses; and car companies said hot summer weather sapped new-car sales, as did stormy winter weather. According to the Dairy Bureau of Canada, weather is the most significant factor in ice-cream sales. We can easily see that cool wet weather can melt ice-cream sales, but then why does chilly Manitoba have the highest per capita consumption of ice cream in Canada?

Sometimes the link between weather and an economic sector is real: for example, the connection between weather and outdoor recreation and tourism is direct and pervasive and it creates both possibilities and limitations. This is why, in 1995, tourist operators in north-central Ontario prayed for a huge snowstorm to save the snowmobiling season: there wasn't enough snow for trails, and many tourists cancelled lodgings because of unseasonably warm weather.

Hot humid weather inside Toronto's SkyDome on August 29, 1990, was said to be responsible for the hoards of dive-bombing bugs who were using the ballpark for a quick mate. The Dome provided them with a huge clearing and relatively calm air ideal for swarming.

For those in the resource industries of farming, fishing and energy, the whims of the weather can spell the difference between prosperity and bankruptcy. The winter of 1993–94's cold weather, average temperature was two to three degrees below normal, meant increased gas shipments and higher profits for gas utilities. Lingering cold winters can shove fuel prices way up because they draw on the gas supply, and like anything in short supply, the gas tends to cost more. In agriculture, the weather cycle and growing cycle are virtually synonymous. Weather is an important factor in a multitude of farm decisions such as what, where and when to sow, irrigate, cultivate, protect and sell; and what equipment to buy or use. To the farmer, weather is the nearest and dearest and most feared companion.

In other instances, the connection—and therefore the rap—is not today's weather, but conditions that occurred last season or a year ago. In 1988, Yukon ranchers blamed the weather for an increase in the number of wolf attacks on livestock that summer: rabbits and other traditional wolf food were killed off by the previous winter's bitter cold. In the summer of 1994, Toronto-area motorists had to endure emergency road repairs, lane restrictions and detours as crews repaired roadways: the deep freeze of January had been especially hard on southern Ontario roads, resulting in the worst outbreak of potholes in at least 30 years. In 1993 and 1994, Ontario's grape crops were at record lows: inclement summer weather in 1993, and the wickedly cold winter in 1994 were blamed.

Faulting the weather is often the easy way out. Full explanations may be much too complex or involve many factors—or else we just don't know. Experts have said that hot weather caused more rattlesnake bites on Manitoulin Island, more fleas in Nova Scotia and more bear attacks on tourists near Churchill. On the other hand, cold weather meant fewer beluga sightings in the Churchill harbour, a massive kill-off of deer in Nova Scotia and elk in Alberta and a lousy pink-salmon season along the West Coast.

People are probably right to blame weather for how they feel. We know, for instance, that weather affects certain diseases such as arthritis and asthma, and is linked to mood disturbances and aggressive behaviour. Death rates from heart attacks are much higher during cold months than at any other time. However, it may be unrealistic for people to blame, as I saw in my collection, extremes of barometric pressure for making people sleepier or hot, humid weather for the sluggish growth of children.

Too often, weather gets an undeserved bad reputation. Here are some even more surprising examples where weather was claimed to be the main culprit:

- Don't blame the chef for flat pastry: apparently without the right weather puff pastry won't rise
- Colonel Gadhafi claimed weather, not terrorists, was responsible for the jet crash over Lockerbie, Scotland
- Fewer babies are born in spring than at any other time; the explanation given is that men produce less sperm in hot summer weather
- Weather is to blame for spelling errors and opening-night jitters

- People are more easily depressed in humid weather
- Weather was blamed for the poor response to a food-bank drive
- Wet cool summers mean fewer butterflies and honeybees
- The Winnipeg post office blamed mail buildup on weather
- In June 1988, hot dry weather in Manitoba made it a bad year for woodticks—so severe was the tick problem that horse owners had to shoot animals covered with bloodsucking parasites
- Mild winters have caused the rat population in Britain to increase by 20 percent
- Because of stormy winter weather in 1994–95, more Ontario Provincial Police officers were busy investigating accidents; this meant fewer cars were pulled over in the program to test for drunk driving
- A hot, dry summer in 1988 more than doubled the price of worms at bait shops in Ontario
- Organizers for a Michael Jackson concert blamed hot weather for Michael's migraine, which led to cancellation of his stage show in the Far East

Adverse weather thousands of kilometres away can be blamed for situations close to home. In 1994–95, Hurricane Gordon destroyed winter vegetables and citrus fruits in Florida, and heavy rains did the same in California. The adverse weather meant an immediate doubling and tripling of fresh fruit and vegetable prices in Canada. In December 1989, cold weather across the United States plains and Midwest caused live hog and cattle futures prices to rise. The cold reduces animals' weight gains and causes farmers to slow deliveries of livestock to slaughterhouses.

Thankfully, weather bashing has become pervasive and universally accepted. How else do you think I can get away with not visiting relatives, or avoiding doing jobs around the house?

BLAME IT ON EL NIÑO—EVERYONE ELSE DOES!

El Niño is not just messing with the world's weather. The menacing "boy child" is at fault for virtually everything bad or abnormal that is happening in the world today. Everything from teachers' strikes to the weak Canadian dollar has been attributed to the warming of the waters in the Pacific Ocean, and many justly so. El Niño....

- increased crime against persons and property (up by 67%) in Saskatoon during the winter
- doubled the number of asthma attacks, and caused an epidemic of migraines among headache sufferers in Calgary
- caused rare "tiger belly" whale beachings in southern China
- encouraged 1.5 million pink flamingos to return to the emerald-green waters of Kenya's Lake Nakuru in the Rift Valley
- caused a shortage of gourmet coffee beans in Colombia
- knocked "The Rosie O'Donnell Show" off the air in a dozen East Coast markets when the satellite feed was interrupted
- brought on an epidemic of skin rashes, itching, burning sensation, swelling and scratching in Kenya due to the emergence of Nairobi fly
- forced the price of soybeans, tofu and anchovies to skyrocket
- inflicted college students in the American Northeast with premature spring fever, making students subsequently flunk midterm exams
- snowed in Guadalajara, Mexico, for the first time since 1881
- decimated the coyote population in Alberta because there were fewer starving and injured deer for them to track down
- destroyed tens of thousands of sea turtle eggs at Playa La Flor, Nicaragua

- confused Pacific sockeye salmon which began showing up ready to spawn in streams where they weren't supposed to be
- raised the passions of people in Guyana, resulting in a rise in domestic violence
- messed up precise astronomical observations because increased water content in the atmosphere alters scientists' data by as much as two percent.
- responsible for malaria, cholera and e. coli in parts of Africa hit by floods; and dengue fever and hantavirus in South America
- killed off huge numbers of boobies (seabirds) and led to the failure in reproduction of albatrosses, penguins and cormorants in the Galapagos
- bloated grapes, resulting in watery, insipid wine
- caused a marked increase in the number of cases of diarrhoea in Peru
- isolated northern communities such as Fort Chipewyan because ice bridges and roads could not be maintained
- sparked grass fires and forest fires for the first time in a decade in Alberta
- caused trees and plants to bud in Alberta in December
- cut into profits of Canadian furriers and caused a 30 percent drop in sales of sandbags, ice-melting salt and automotive products like batteries and tires; also caused substantial decrease in winter boot sales in Canada (although western footwear is ahead)
- all but whipped out the ice fishing in the lower Great Lakes and inland Ontario lakes, and forced the cancellation of the traditional polar-bear dip at Sylvan Lake because the ice was dangerously thin.
- forced up the price of broccoli, lettuce and cauliflower by 3 1/2 times in Saskatchewan

Being practical
about weather

Over millions of years, different climates have shaped landforms, laying down carbon deposits, feeding glaciers, sustaining rivers and producing soils. In addition, there is scarcely one aspect of society and the economy that is not affected, in some way, by climate and by climate change and by the day-to-day influences of weather. Foremost, atmospheric changes provide life's essentials: heat, moisture and light.

The march of diurnal temperature and moisture and the progression of the seasons influence dress, what we eat, how we feel and behave, the cost of heating or cooling our homes and our vacation plans. By influencing market supply and demand, it can create inflation, financial crises and social unrest. It is essential to the production of trees, the growth of crops, the success of the fishery and the management of water resources. Used to plan and design, weather and climate can make for safer and more comfortable activities and more profitably run operations.

Guests at a Myrtle Beach, South Carolina, resort can buy insurance against rainy weather, provided that they do so 14 days before their vacation begins. The premium against rainy days amounts to $5 for every $100 of coverage.

Because it restricts agriculture, fisheries and forestry to specific geographical areas, climate has influenced human migration and settlement. Through drought and flood, climate can destroy and debilitate life, damage property and isolate entire communities.

There are many untold examples of good planning through the proper application of meteorology. Just the fact that buildings aren't collapsing daily under climate stresses or that crops everywhere aren't failing is evidence that applying good climate knowledge and information greatly benefits humankind. Climate and weather information is of enormous economic worth in such activities as farming, recreation, energy and transportation, providing answers to such questions as: How much should be budgeted for snow removal? Are there sufficient hours of wind blow to sustain a wind-driven generator? Which climates are best for people suffering from asthma or arthritis? Will peaches grow in Kapuskasing or cabbages in Whitehorse? Is there enough snowfall for a successful ski resort? What impact will the effects of global warming have on sea-level rise in Prince Edward Island and traditional native life in the Arctic?

By answering these questions, using decades of weather records collected by observers across Canada and more recently, by data from satellites, aircraft, radar and other sources, climatologists serve the needs of many sectors of the Canadian economy.

The following sections contain examples of how climate and weather data, information and services have benefited those in selected weather-sensitive sectors or activities.

Agriculture, Forestry and Fisheries

Weather affects humankind most closely in farming. Crops that are economically viable in Canada include fruit trees in the Okanagan, wheat and oilseeds on the Prairies, corn and grapes in southern Ontario and Quebec, and potatoes and apples in the Maritimes. Only tropical and equatorial crops cannot be grown commercially. To be successful, a farmer must minimize risk from climate hazards by avoiding the risk in the first place or by protecting against the hazard when it threatens.

All agricultural areas in Canada are subject to drought, frost, winterkill, wind, heavy precipitation, hail and flooding, and to climatically influenced diseases and insect infestations. Evaluation of lands where climate is suitable for special crops is an important application of climate knowledge and information.

Climate and weather influence a host of farming operations, including seeding, irrigating, spraying, cultivating, harvesting and scheduling labour. Post-harvest concerns of crop storage and transportation and livestock performance are also affected by weather conditions. Few question the importance of accurate and timely weather forecasts to the agriculture and food-growing business. Simple climate data, such as growing degree-days and drying indices, have found wide application in improving many farm-management operations. More complex crop-yield models are also widely used by growers and by agronomists and economists in agencies such as the Canadian Wheat Board, Prairie Farm

Rehabilitation Administration and various grain cooperatives in order to forecast growing conditions and develop marketing strategies. A recent development is the monitoring of climates and related information abroad for capitalizing on global trading and marketing opportunities.

Climate is no less a controlling agent in tree production. Foresters seek current weather data and information in protecting against hazards such as drought, excess water, fire, frost, blow-down, air pollution, pests and diseases. The monitoring of fire-weather parameters—moisture conditions of the soil and ground litter, wind speed and direction, humidity and thunderstorm activity—are especially crucial in forest-fire prevention and control. And in combating pests and diseases through aerial spraying, such as spruce budworm operations in New Brunswick, synoptic weather conditions, such as the onset and duration of the sea breeze, are crucial in deciding spray strategies.

Longer-term climate information, both historic and projected, are eagerly sought by forest managers because meteorology affects the growth of trees at every stage from planting to harvesting, and influences forest management practices, including site preparation, regeneration, thinning and fertilizing. Regeneration of forests takes decades, and to ensure future supplies of trees it is important that varieties be selected to optimize climate potential. No better

Delineation of areas where climate is suitable for special crops is an important application of climatology. For example, canola seed is a $2 billion business in western Canada, where the prairie climate of hot sunny days and cool nights is ideally suited to intensive canola production. To the south, the percentage of oil in the seed drops off, so that growing it becomes uneconomical as far north as Minneapolis.

example exists of the need for information on climate change and variability than forestry. After all, trees are likely to be harvested in weather conditions much different from those that prevailed during planting.

The size of fish stocks and their migration patterns are greatly influenced by changes in oceanographic and atmospheric parameters. Climate data could have important economic benefits to the fishery through improved understanding of the onset of ice formation and ice breakup and the distribution and migration of various commercial fish species, and improved access to fishery grounds. Careful monitoring of currents, temperature and other oceanographic factors can save millions of dollars because slight changes can have tremendous impact on the size and migration patterns of fish species in a certain area. For example, in the late 1970s, Canadian fishing fleets missed the mackerel run on the East Coast. Three-quarters of a million dollars was wasted in deployment costs and $5 million in revenues were lost. A capacity to predict monthly and seasonal variations would greatly enhance the tactical planning of fishing-fleet operations and would improve the management of the fisheries.

The John Hancock Mutual Life Insurance Company headquarters in Boston lost a third of its insulating glass double window panes before occupancy. Poor climate design was the principal reason for the failure. Every single window was replaced with heat-treated glass—total cost $10 million.

Water Resources

Precipitation is the source of all the earth's fresh water, and evaporation is the primary moisture input into the atmosphere. Canada contains no large areas where annual evaporation greatly exceeds precipitation, producing permanent deserts, or where precipitation greatly exceeds evaporation, resulting in annual flooding. Canada has more usable fresh water than any other country in the world; however, the water demand is so great that climate variations are of concern to those involved in securing water supplies.

Climate is a principal factor in determining the water-resources potential of a region. Satisfying the demand for water, and in amounts that avoid flood or drought hazards, requires design data and credible climate data and weather forecasts. On the Prairies, farmers anxious about water for irrigation and municipal officials worried about flooding regularly seek information about the winter's snowpack and spring rains.

Engineers on the Great Lakes make daily assessments of the basin's water balance in order to predict lake-level changes and regulate flows.

More precise definition of climate parameters would improve water supply, and demand forecasts and in turn realize enormous savings in power generation at Niagara Falls and in scheduling drafts of ships on the St. Lawrence Seaway. For example, a 2.5 centimetre reduction in lake levels would necessitate a reduction of more than 180 tonnes per ship of Class 10 (305 metres) plying that waterway or a loss of about one million tonnes of shipping capacity per season. In Canada, the export of hydroelectricity is big business, and electric utilities count on ample winter precipitation to fill reservoirs. Manitoba Hydro estimated losses of $80 million in power it was unable to produce and export due to deficiencies of snow cover in the spring of 1981. Credible climate forecasts would have allowed abnormally high water storage in the preceding season and relevant operating strategies to avoid the loss. In moist regions with a reliable streamflow, engineers develop schemes for diverting surpluses to water-starved regions.

Energy Consumption

Canada consumes more energy per capita than any other country, the equivalent of nine tonnes of oil annually. This thirst for energy is caused largely by Canada's vast distances, its resource-based economy and its climate extremes. About a third of the energy now used in Canada is expended to offset the cold, ice and snow of winter, and the heat and humidity of summer. In the 1970s and 1980s, severe winters and uncertainty of foreign oil supplies focused attention on Canada's vulnerability to climate change and variability.

Further cooling or increased snow would cost the Canadian economy dearly; on the other hand, a warming of 2°C to 3°C would decrease winter heating needs by about 15 percent, the equivalent of 45 million barrels of oil, an annual saving of $1.5 billion. The safe and economic exploitation of energy reserves, be they offshore in Hibernia, high on a mountain slope or inland in the oil sands, demands good climate information. A large petroleum exploration company drilling off the Labrador coast in 1974–76 found that only one or two days were lost each season by having to move their drill ship off site to avoid icebergs (despite using other ships to tow potentially dangerous icebergs away from the well site). Had the climate information relating to iceberg size, frequency and movement not been incorporated into initial design work, a conventional moored drill ship might have been used and could have been completely lost, due to its being unable to move off site quickly enough. A capital loss of up to $250 million would have resulted, not to mention the possible loss of human life and the potential environmental impacts of an oil spill.

Furthermore, climate-related applications are not restricted to energy exploration and development: electric-power transmission lines are sensitive to icing, lightning and tornadoes; and construction and operation of pipelines in permafrost depend on changes of temperature and soil moisture.

Another issue is how much of Canada's energy needs can be met by renewable sources. Passive solar heating could reduce energy bills. Inexhaustible, pollution-free wind energy, once very popular, could again supply much of the energy needs of small, remote communities. In achieving energy conservation, climate information is of use in the planning of potential sites, the design of material and the operation of facilities.

Building and Construction

In most countries, the building and construction sector is the largest single industry. From the viewpoint of safety and economy, a structure or facility must be able to withstand meteorological forces and loadings over its lifetime and take steady wear and tear during normal times and during extremely unusual events. Overdesign is wasteful and costly; underdesign can be hazardous and result in discomfort.

Architects, engineers, builders and planners are often guilty of placing structures suitable for one climate in a very different one—for example, California-style homes in Edmonton. Climate information is useful in determining the orientation of buildings so that there is minimum energy loss and reduced snow drifting, and in designing buildings that have comfortable, healthful, safe and economical indoor climates. At a large Canadian hardware distribution centre near Lester Pearson International Airport in Toronto, loading docks were designed to keep them clear of snow, thus cutting snow-removal bills and minimizing disruption times.

Climate data are used in support of national building codes to obviate structural failures due to climate stresses and to ensure adequate heating and ventilation. The reduction in the amount of concrete to be poured, in the capacity for backup energy supply or in the thickness of transmission cables and guide wires can save millions of dollars in individual projects.

Such information can also help in the choice of safe, economical materials that will withstand damage by strong winds, driving rain or frequent freeze-thaw temperature changes. Home-owners can realize greater comfort and reduced energy costs by considering such questions as where to plant trees in order to provide shelter from winter winds and to keep driveways free of snow; what sort of curtains to choose in order to keep out unwanted summer heat; or which wall of the house should contain a large area of glass to let in winter sun.

A valley-bottom site was first selected for the Yukon mining town of Faro until climatologists pointed out the preference for a location 60 to 90 metres above the valley floor to take advantage of milder temperatures within the slope of the Arctic inversion. Higher winter temperatures have resulted in lower fuel costs, fewer vehicle stoppages and higher morale among the people.

Transportation

Water, land or air transportation is influenced by climate variability or extremes. Route planning and scheduling and cargo handling and storage all depend upon sound climate information. In marine areas, sea ice, poor visibility and storm occurrence are significant problems and affect the design and operation of ships and port facilities. Design must incorporate information about storms—for example, that which sank the *Ocean Ranger* oil rig off Newfoundland, drowning 84 men on February 15, 1982—in order to defend against such hazards. Metallurgical changes induced by persistent cold led to the failure of a drilling platform off Norway, with the loss of about 100 lives and the capital investment of about $1.25 billion. Better climate data in design could have prevented the collapse.

Freezing and thawing, precipitation and snow cover are very important to land transportation by road, rail or pipeline. Annual snow-removal costs may exceed $1 billion in Canada. Knowledge of the normal distribution of snowfall and its relative frequency of occurrence during the day and over the season is of great assistance to highway-system designers in locating maintenance depots, designing snow-removal equipment and scheduling work periods for crews. Air transportation has always been concerned with wind, ceiling, visibility and turbulence, whether for airport siting, timing of favourable takeoffs and landings or en-route aircraft operations.

In communications, examples abound of the enormous savings through the proper application of climate information. In 1969, a section of the Quebec-Labrador powerline had to be replaced at a cost of $30 million. The stress from ice and wind loading had not been accounted for properly in the original design. A more accurate wind-load design for a communication tower in Alberta saved $70,000 in repair costs, and more accurate snow-load data for one arena roof in Saskatchewan saved $25,000. The design of Toronto's CN Tower was altered when climatologists predicted icefall from the antennae.

Health and Recreation

One of the most interesting and challenging areas of modern climatology deals with the effects of climate on human health. As we have noted, climate-related health problems include the common cold, hypothermia, hay fever, asthma, frostbite and migraine complaints. Even more common are subtle climate-induced or climate-intensified sickness, fatigue, pain, seasonal adjustment disorder (SAD) and insomnia, all of which ultimately diminish alertness, learning ability, performance and productivity.

Climatic factors are also pervasive in the field of recreation and tourism. Many communities, and even entire countries, are dependent on the income from tourism. For developing countries, tourism is a major source of foreign exchange and it provides important income generation and employment opportunities. The economic well-being of vacation areas depends upon the occurrence of expected weather. Travel agencies and resort complexes use climate data to choose suitable sites for business meetings and conferences and the times for peak activity.

Downhill skiing is particularly sensitive to the variability of snowfall. The absence of snow generally keeps people from skiing despite snow-making equipment, and a lack of snow between Christmas and New Year's Day can spell disaster for resort operators. Climate information has been used in the siting and design of trails and the design of equipment and facilities; in assessment of competing sites for sporting events; and in the scheduling of games and contests. Parks Canada planners scrapped plans to build a mechanical stairway from the Kluane Lake Basin to the summit of Kluane Mountain Range at a cost of $2 million. Historical data indicated that the frequency of summer cloudiness would preclude viewing the spectacular ice fields 80 percent of the time. In another example, a climatologist advised local resort promoters interested in developing a snowmobile park to avoid the proposed site where only 10 to 20 days a year could be counted on for sufficient snow cover; a second site with favourable snow conditions was recommended, and the resort was built there.

Industry and Commerce

In spite of the fact that meteorological knowledge and information can profitably be applied to a broad span of industry, commerce and financial services, most managers in these areas largely ignore weather and climate when making economic decisions. They dismiss weather because they see it operating in some random fashion, and because, they believe, there are too many other more important variables to consider. For example, climatologists can assist insurance companies in establishing the degree of risk for natural hazards (wind, hail, floods) and hence the premiums to be levied, together with expert

The climate has its economic significance. In a typical winter, Montreal may spend $50 million on snow removal, whereas Victoria may spend only a few thousand. For farmers and ski-lodge operators, the whims of the weather can spell the difference between prosperity and bankruptcy. Because of the extremes of our climate, we are also among the world's largest energy users and probably the world's most enthusiastic developers of indoor and underground shopping centres.

advice in settling claims. Climate information is also used by business and industry to make critical choices concerning delivery and stockpiling of raw materials, production and marketing, and by stockbrokers and commodity traders in buying and selling.

Most large national retailers are aware of the average dates of significant weather events in each market area and therefore have consumer goods and advertising ready in these localities at these times. Climate-sensitive products such as bathing suits, kites, skis, ice cream and antifreeze should be marketed near areas where they are most useful and in the appropriate season for successful results. Automobile manufacturers use precipitation data to study windshield-wiper performance on passenger cars, and they change door-handle design to minimize freeze-up for automobiles sold in places with extremely cold winters.

With such an important array of beneficial uses, it is surprising that relatively few people are aware of the enormous potential and economic worth of using weather data and information beyond whether it will rain on the weekend or the coming winter will be long and cold. Using information about weather and climate wisely will help enhance our management of resources. Used to plan and design, meteorology can make for safer and more comfortable activities and more profitably run operations.

FROSTBITE

In the last week of February 1994, a vicious blizzard plunged southeastern Saskatchewan into a deep freeze. At 2 a.m. on February 23, two-year-old Karlee Kosolofski of Rouleau, Saskatchewan, wandered out the front door of her parents' bungalow and was accidentally locked outside in a wind chill that froze her flesh in 30 seconds. Six hours later, her mother found her apparently lifeless body. Her subsequent recovery, from severe hypothermia and frostbite, is perhaps the most publicized account of cold-weather injury in recent times.

Doctors later estimated Karlee's core body temperature fell to 14°C, some 24 degrees below normal. Miraculously, medical staff at the Plains Health Centre in Regina brought the youngster back to life by artificially warming her blood with a heart and lung machine. Little Karlee made the *Guinness Book of Records* for surviving the lowest-recorded body temperature.

Her frostbite injuries were much more serious. Doctors said her legs had the brick-like consistency of freezer meat when she was found. Ten days later, her left leg was amputated below the knee. She also had minor frostbite to her nose, ears and right elbow.

Elderly people may be threatened by a subtle form of hypothermia—core body temperature below 35˚C—if the indoor room temperature is too cool for them.

Thousands of Canadians suffer from frostbite. In the winter of 1991–92, 253 people were hospitalized with frostbite: 80 percent were male and 20 percent female; 5 percent had face injuries, 30 percent hands, 58 percent feet, and 7 percent of injuries were unspecified.

Frostbite is the freezing of the skin and underlying body tissue after exposure to temperatures below freezing. It's almost exclusively a human injury. Cold-adapted animals such as wolves, caribou and polar bears have sufficient blood and heat flow in their extremities to prevent freezing at –70˚C. Extremities—fingers, toes, ears, the nose and chin—are often the first to freeze because they protrude and have relatively poor circulation. Knees, legs, shins, cheeks and the forehead are also vulnerable. Exposure to extreme cold in itself does not necessarily lead to frostbite. But cold combined with exhaustion, shock, hunger, dehydration, injury, prolonged immobility or clothing that is inadequate or constricts blood flow can lead to frostbite. Alcohol consumption before exposure is also a factor, in many cases.

The U.S. Navy manual issued to personnel going to the Arctic and Antarctic states, "Do not touch cold metal with moist, bare hands. If you should inadvertently stick a hand to cold metal, urinate on the metal to warm it and save some inches of skin."

Frostbite has plagued soldiers for centuries, because they live outdoors in all weather, are often wounded or tired and frequently have insufficient food, water and warm clothing. The armies of Hannibal and Napoleon lost thousands

---

What to Do If You're Stranded in a Car

- Stay with the car—it's your best shelter.
- Make sure that the exhaust pipe is free of snow; otherwise, deadly carbon monoxide fumes can back up into the pipe.
- Run the engine for 10 minutes every hour. This should keep you sufficiently warm, while keeping the battery charged and conserving gas.
- Keep a window partly open for air when the car is running.
- Make your car visible with a flare or warning light. Even a scarf tied to the aerial will help.

---

to the cold. During the Crimean War, French troops suffered more than 5,000 cases of frostbite, and during the Korean War a quarter of all American casualties suffered cold injury, mostly frostbite, trench foot and hypothermia. Among polar travellers of the last century, frostbite was quite common.

Today, frostbite is much less prevalent than it was even two decades ago. One noted expert on cold weather injury, Dr. Murray Hamlet of the United States Army Research Institute of Environmental Medicine near Boston, suggests a host of reasons for the decline: the public is better informed about cold weather survival, fewer wars are fought at high latitudes, more students are bused to school and better outdoor clothing, equipment and central heating are being used. However, for those who work, travel and play in the cold, frostbite is still a serious risk. Street people are also at high risk as are people stranded by stalled vehicles or accidents. Elderly persons and the very young are particulary vulnerable to frostbite. Seniors are at risk because they are usually less active and unable to move around to maintain their circulation adequately. Children have a large surface-area-to-body-mass ratio and tend to cool fast.

Our environment and weather create frostbite risk with freezing temperatures, moisture and wind chill. The degree of frostbite depends, naturally, on the severity and duration of cold stress. (Temperatures must be below $-0.5°C$ before flesh will freeze.) Moisture can contribute to heat loss in two ways. When exposed skin becomes wet, body heat evaporates the moisture, which chills the skin (also why we feel a chill while towelling off). Second, moist clothing draws heat away from our bodies, which is why a cold damp day often feels colder than a cold dry one.

You can lose 50 to 70 percent of your body heat through the top of your head because it has so many blood vessels and very little fat. Wear a hat in cold, windy weather. Cowboy hats and baseball caps are okay, but a toque, balaclava or parka hood are much better.

Wind chill is a measure of the air's cooling power—the effective temperature of wind plus cold, not simply the air temperature. Our bodies are enveloped in a very thin layer of still air that insulates us against colder outer air. Without any wind, this warmed air stays next to the skin. But that insulating layer can be thinned or blown away by the wind. That makes more cold air contact the skin than the body can counteract with its own heat, and we feel a chill. A temperature of –20°C combined with a wind speed of 50 kilometres per hour feels like –44°C. At that wind-chill temperature, exposed skin can freeze in under a minute.

What happens when you develop frostbite? As your extremities begin to chill, the blood vessels in your skin constrict in order to prevent warm blood from flowing to the surface and losing its heat. Without heat, your skin tissue freezes. The thin blood vessels beneath the frozen tissue also constrict, reducing blood supply. Simultaneously, the body dehydrates as water is withdrawn from the cells by osmosis, thickening the blood. This thickened blood cannot travel through the narrower blood vessels, and the flow is cut off or diverted from the extremity. As the water freezes within the tissues, the ice crystals damage blood vessels, and biochemical changes damage the tissue. Rapid freezing does less harm, since it creates smaller crystals. That Karlee froze solid in 20 minutes may have saved her life.

As with burns, several degrees of frostbite are recognized, although most experts classify injuries as either superficial or deep. Frostnip (first degree, or superficial frostbite) is the mildest form, and seldom leads to permanent injury. At this early stage, the victim is often unaware of the injury, except for some numbness. There may be some local itching or burning and tenderness, and the skin may look pale and waxy.

Second-degree frostbite freezes tissue beneath the outer layer of skin. The frostnipped tissue may be cold and hard to the touch. Thawing can bring excruciating pain. Sometimes swelling occurs, and clear, superficial blisters erupt a day or two after exposure; in about a week, the blisters dry, and in a month, a layer of pinkish skin forms.

In a study of 101 patients suffering frostbite who were admitted to hospitals in Saskatoon during 10 winters, researchers found that alcohol consumption was a causative factor in 39 patients and a motor vehicle accident or breakdown in 33 others.

Often, third- or fourth-degree frostbite involves damage to deeper tissues including nerve, blood vessels, muscle and bone. With a loss of nerves, there is sometimes an absence of pain. To the touch, the damaged skin feels woody and lifeless. In a few days, dark ugly blood blisters may cover the entire affected area, signalling the death of skin and possibly of deeper tissue. The affected part remains swollen and discoloured. Eventually, gangrene sets in and the dead tissue simply falls off.

Once you've had frostbite, you are more likely to get it again, since the blood vessels never regain their full size after recovery. But this increased sensitivity to cold can actually reduce future risks. Sakiasie Sowdlooapik, visitor service officer at the Auyuittuq National Park Reserve on Baffin Island, confirmed an old Inuit custom of intentionally exposing ears to cause frostnip, in order to acquire the subsequent "early-warning" system for frostbite.

After recovery, frostbite victims often experience persistent pain, excessive sweating, burning or itching. In the long term, some people report arthritis in affected bones and cancer in scar tissue. Amputation of desiccated tissue may be necessary as a last resort. Unfortunately, amputation is often done too soon, before the tissue has had a chance to recover.

Frostnip can be treated on the spot by blowing hot breath on the affected part; holding nipped fingertips in the armpits; and placing warm hands over the ears or cheeks. Forget that old folk remedy of rubbing snow or applying ice on frostbitten skin: it doesn't work, and just

Pet-Safety Tips

Pets get frostbite too, and need extra care on cold icy days. Here are some pet-safety tips for the cold weather:

- Cats are best kept inside, as are most small and short-haired dogs
- On cold days, apply Vaseline to a pet's paw pads before it goes out; in winter, wash ice, salts and other chemicals from your pet's pads once it's back inside
- An outdoor dog needs a dry, elevated doghouse with clean, dry bedding and a flap over the opening to keep the wind out
- Check outdoor water bowls often when it's freezing; do not use metal dishes for food and water — the tongue, nose and lips can stick to such surfaces
- Do not allow pets to eat snow on city streets or drink from puddles
- Outdoor dogs need more calories in winter to produce body heat, so give them more food; indoor dogs and cats may get less exercise in cold months and will need fewer calories
- Antifreeze tastes good to pets but is a deadly poison
- If it is too cold for you to go outside, it is too cold for your pet

might inflict permanent injury. Someone once described rubbing ice on frozen skin was like grinding glass into the skin. Nor should you try to warm a frostbitten appendage from a campfire, heat lamp, hot stove, exhaust pipe, a hot-water bottle or other source of dry heat: since your skin cannot feel the heat, you could easily burn yourself.

Deep frostbite is a serious injury that requires immediate medical attention.

Frostbite risk is reason to respect, but not fear, the cold. Guard against the effects of cold, moisture and wind by wearing clothing in multiple layers rather than a single heavy outer garment, and especially covering your hands, feet and head, through which as much as 55 percent of total body heat is lost. Surviving in the cold is a matter of having common sense and being alert, prepared and properly equipped.

One should always have an eye for the weather. Be aware not only of the air temperature but the wind speed, because strong winds make it feel colder than it actually is and increase the rate of heat loss. In addition, overexertion will produce excessive perspiration that will lead to evaporation and heat loss.

Back in Rouleau, little Karlee Kosolofski has been fitted with a prosthesis attached below her left knee, and has learned to walk all over again. As for the terrible ordeal, her amazing recovery and the attention paid her case worldwide, her father, Robert, reports that Karlee would rather talk about school or tease her older sister and brother.

PROFITING FROM
WEATHER

Here's a hot stock-market tip! Buy when it's raining or overcast and prices are depressed. Sell in the sunshine when traders and investors feel better, buy more and in doing so bid up the price.

Just like the weather, prices of stock on the Toronto Stock Exchange and other exchanges vary considerably and reflect many things, including the economy, prices and interest rates, the jobless figure, elections, international news, what prominent investors, politicians and bankers say or do not say and the weather.

Weather? Well, it's not one of the more immediate factors that come to mind in explaining stock-market behaviour. Atmospheric pressure and storms are usually lumped in with factors such as sunspots and phases of the moon—somewhere between "market exuberance" and the height of hemlines.

Few investors would consider that there is any link between weather events and the rise and fall of the stock market, even though weather can make a big difference in a company's earnings. Because weather is highly related to demand, supply and production, the financial performance of retailers and utilities, for instance, can be tied closely to weather anomalies. Consequently, entrepreneurs and investors should be concerned with weather, especially before it actually occurs.

Astute market watchers spend considerable time following the highs and lows on the weather news because they realize only too well that weather—especially severe storms and insidious events like droughts and floods—do affect how some companies and key economic sectors perform.

Obviously, some sectors and businesses are more interested in weather reports than others. Breweries, ice-cream parlours and swimming-pool installers revel in hot weather because it traditionally pushes up sales. Ski-resort operators rejoice at an early heavy snowfall. And investors with stocks in snowblowers and snow shovels, or cold remedies and tissues, get quite excited at an unusual spell of tough winter!

Clearly affected by weather extremes is the insurance industry. A bad year for hailstorms, tornadoes and freezing rain means insurance companies have to pay more to their policyholders, which has a negative result for shareholders. But the same storms can drive lumber and building material prices and profits through the ceiling. That is exactly what happened in August 1992 after Hurricane Andrew struck south Florida. Damage losses, mostly to homes and buildings, cost $35 billion. But this was a bonanza for the lumber industry in North America, as demand and sales of building materials soared at a time when business is usually slow.

On February 11, 1994, a severe winter storm dumped heavy snow across the Eastern Seaboard and forced the New York Stock Exchange, the American Stock Exchange, the NASDAQ market and others to take the highly unusual step of stopping operations. It was the first time weather had halted trading since a hurricane struck New York in 1985.

Another industry very affected by weather is agriculture, with its extremely volatile prices. A mere hint of a deep freeze or rumour of coming rains can rattle the markets and send the price of food commodities on a rise and dive as undulating as the jet stream. Traders stand to make or lose millions of dollars, depending on news that it's too wet, too dry or too cold. Hence, in 1996, the simple beginning of the frost season in Brazil was enough to quadruple the price of coffee beans in New York. And at the beginning of the major North American drought

A finance professor at the University of Massachusetts and former stockbroker analyzed 28 years of weather data and compared the data with the daily indexes on the New York and American Stock Exchanges. On sunny days, he found the indexes were up more than 57 percent of the time, whereas under cloudy skies the indexes were up less than 50 percent of the time.

in 1988, a meteorologist created quite a stir when he went outside for a cup of coffee. From his office at Smith Barney Inc. in Chicago, Jon Davis inadvertently moved markets when he donned his trench coat. Said Davis to *The Wall Street Journal*, "I had to walk past the traders to get out, and everyone figured this was some kind of secret signal, that I thought the weather would break and start raining and maybe they should sell the market. In fact, it was a cool day in May and I'd put the coat on because it was chilly."

Those investing and trading in oil and gas also hang on every weather word. When winters are cold, people use more natural gas to warm their houses and businesses. The more natural gas people use, the more profit for the gas company. After the eruption of Mount Pinatubo in the Philippines in June 1991, global temperatures declined by more than 0.5°C over the next two years, enough to produce colder winters in parts of North America and Europe. That single eruption on the other side of the world did more to quadruple the price of natural gas—and earn billions of dollars for the industry—than the Gulf War or any United Nations embargo. Likewise, late in 1996, the Toronto Stock Exchange's oil and gas index rose by 20 percent, largely because of Environment Canada's winter outlook, which called for a colder three months ahead than normal—a prospect that would likely boost oil and natural gas demand and increase producers' profits.

The commodities market, however, is perhaps the best example of weather sensitivity in the business world. Commodity traders deal in buying and selling contracts to deliver such commodities as soybeans, frozen orange juice, gold, tea, hogs or natural gas. The goods are never seen by those who buy and sell. That's because the market works on futures or options. Traders buy and sell the right to buy or sell a given amount of the commodity for delivery at a set time in the future at a guaranteed price. They are betting on the short-term price of the commodities in the hope of profiting from price changes. For example, one trader might agree to buy 5,000 bushels of Canadian soybeans at $8 a bushel in 90 days. This assures the soybean growers a certain guaranteed profit, while the trader hopes that the price will rise in the meantime, so that from now until the end of the period he or she can either sell the contract or the soybeans at a higher price. That's why broccoli growers and natural-gas consumers may curse the cold, but those investors who profit from ballooning prices bless it.

The futures market is a kind of insurance against price swings, including those related to weather. This market enables people who actually trade in produce and goods—for example, farmers, sugar refineries and gas utilities—to reduce the risk they face of losing money because of changes in the price of commodities they haven't yet produced, as in the case of the producer, or raw materials they haven't yet received, in the case of the manufacturer. Since the price at which futures in a commodity will be bought and sold depends on the supply and the supply depends, among other things, on weather in the producing area, most people involved in commodities should be keenly interested in what the future weather will be. Veteran traders tell you the first thing they do in the morning is check the weather forecast at home and overseas.

To gain that competitive advantage, some commodity firms even hire their own private meteorologists to get the detailed weather reports and exclusivity they need. Some meteorologists, like James Roemer of Raleigh, North Carolina, a former television weather broadcaster, have successfully combined forecasting and trading. They tell their newsletter or hot-line subscribers not only what the weather will be but also what to do about it.

Not everyone thinks it's proper for practising meteorologists to be dabbling in the markets. Something about insider trading! Some meteorologists, though, are so confident of their forecasts that they have parlayed weather hunches into big windfalls. Said one meteorologist-trader, "Orange juice and pork bellies put my children through school."

What really practical information can the meteorologist provide the investor-trader? It's not likely to be today's weather forecast—that's available to everyone. What customers really need is precise and detailed, preferably exclusive, information on weather here and elsewhere, what effect current weather will have on the commodity and what the weather will be in a few weeks or few months from now.

In preparing the investor's weather report, the meteorologist sifts through stacks of charts and data from around the world. The forecaster monitors satellite imagery, follows weather systems in the upper atmosphere, monitors surface water temperatures in the tropical oceans and consults historical records. For those monitoring grains and livestock futures, contemporary weather data are then converted into projections of crop growth and yield potential. That's why the Canadian Wheat Board actively keeps tabs on the competition—weather anomalies in the United States corn belt, the success or failure of the Indian monsoon and the severity of drought in Australia and Russia.

Monitoring developing and evolving weather conditions such as drought and flooding, and assessing crop health abroad for governments and traders have become necessary activities in order to avoid a repeat of the Great Grain Robbery of 1972. That year, drought and massive crop failures in the Soviet Union led government officials to purchase 20 million tonnes or nearly 10 percent of the North American grain crop at bargain prices. No one knew how serious the drought and the lack of snow was in the grain-growing territory of the Soviet Union. The subsequent disappearance of grain from the market caused food prices to rise sharply in North America in spite of a bumper harvest and a tripling of world cereal prices. The result was regional famine in Africa and South Asia, a scramble for available grain reserves, market speculation and widespread inflation.

Without question, future weather is the weather intelligence investors most eagerly seek. Brokers and traders know it's much easier to predict tomorrow's Dow Jones average than those for next month. The same holds true for meteorologists trying to forecast into the future. As the time period of the forecast is extended, the level of accuracy drops steadily. It is well known that as soon as a prediction is made beyond seven days, it can only be marginally better than chance.

All long-lead forecasting methods are controversial and not widely accepted. Generally, commodity weather analysts shy away from global circulation models of the atmosphere and ocean that use complex mathematical equations to simulate the atmosphere. They have their own "quick and dirty" methods and don't rely on the national weather service.

Most private meteorologists use analogue and statistical methods to forecast future weather. The analogue approach is based on the belief that weather patterns repeat. The technique involves matching, say, this autumn with a previous autumn and inferring that perhaps this winter will be similar to that previous year's winter. The trick is to find a previous year that is a perfect match, and that's difficult. True analogues are both rare and poorly behaved.

A statistical method that uses several past years of data is the most common approach to forecasting weather a month or season ahead. Certain abnormalities in the weather are more persistent than others, and certain geographical patterns of weather tend to recur. Trends, cycles and rhythms do appear in long-term climatic records. The statistical relationships that are found, though, are generally weak, and it is a difficult problem for scientists to determine which of the observed relationships are reliable and which are chance coincidence in the data.

Because weather only repeats itself from year to year about 35 percent of the time, retailers who predict sales based on the previous year's weather will be wrong two seasons out of three.

Jon Miller of Smith Barney found that after the 10 warmest winters in 100 years in the United States, 8 of the following summers were warmer than normal with 5 of the 10 ranking in the top 20 warmest summers of all time. On the other hand, only 2 of the following winters were warmer than normal, 3 were close to normal and 5 were colder than normal. He also found that extremely warm summers nationwide tend to lead to mild winters across the United States.

But not so in Canada! Based on an analysis of temperature records across Canada for this century, for 10 of the warmest winters, 4 of the following summers were near normal, 3 were warmer and 3 were cooler than normal. Similarly, there was no clear connection to the follow-

The Blizzard of '96 wasn't all bad for retailers. Whereas severe winter weather causes certain losses, customers often cheer themselves up by making large purchases. In the entertainment and food sectors, the big storm was a boon to video rental stores and for takeout-food vendors, while gambling casinos in Atlantic City—some of which were forced to close—saw a loss of business.

ing winter. Half of the next winters were milder than normal, 3 were colder and 2 were about average. There was a tendency for cool summers to follow cold winters, but it was not very significant. And if the winter had seasonable temperatures, there was an equal chance that the following summer would experience below, near or above normal temperatures; in other words, anything was possible.

Other statistical methods have attempted to correlate weather and sunspot activity. For example, James Roemer found that years immediately following minimum sunspot activity typically were colder than normal in the United States. Persistence is another seasonal forecasting method consulting forecasters use. It implies a continuation of current conditions—that is, what you see is what you're going to get.

A very promising area of research in long-range forecasting concerns teleconnections—linkages between weather changes occurring in widely separated regions of the globe often many thousands of kilometres apart. The best known teleconnection is El Niño.

El Niño seems to have something for everyone. It has been blamed for droughts in Indonesia and Brazil, bush fires in Australia, flooding rains in Chile and Peru and the failure of the Indian monsoon. In persisting for 12 to 18 months, El Niño can seriously affect a country's food supply and water resources.

In temperate latitudes over North America, the impacts of El Niño show up most clearly during the winter. For example, most El Niño winters are mild over western Canada and parts of the northern United States, and wet over California and the southern United States from Texas to Florida. The warm El Niño tends to strengthen the jet stream as it flows from west to east across the Pacific and North America. This enhanced jet stream blocks cold air from penetrating down into the heart of the continent, leaving most of southern Canada in a milder and drier than normal weather regime. How certain is the warmth across Canada with an El Niño? El Niño effects depend largely on how warm the ocean's surface water gets and how large an area of the Pacific warms up.

Forecasting El Niño's duration and precise effects is difficult. You can't say whether this one will be worse than the previous one. It never stays the same; neither do the impacts. In some cases, though, the direct association between El Niño warming and weather is quite predictable and measurable.

An examination of the five warmest and five coldest winters across the Prairies, British Columbia and Yukon over the past 50 years reveals that in the five warmest winters, there is a very strong correlation between winter mildness and El Niño occurrence. Of the five warmest winters, there was an El Niño event during four of them; the other warm winter occurred when sea surface temperatures were near normal. The correlation during an unusually cold winter is almost as dramatic. Of the five coldest winters across the west and northwest, three occurred during a cold El Niño phase and the other two were neutral. (A cold El Niño phase is not an El Niño—it's often called La Niña.) When there is a warm El Niño event, the odds significantly favour a warm winter in the west. However, the warming pattern would extend farther eastward only with a strong El Niño.

Armed with information about an emerging El Niño, farmers around the world would be better able to assess their risks, and make changes to planting strategies in anticipation of severe farming conditions. Watching El Niño and acting before the weather changes could also earn economic benefits to commodities traders.

When El Niño is brewing, meteorologists believe they can make reasonably accurate, credible and timely weather forecasts for many months ahead and assess the impacts that warming will have on many vulnerable regions around the world. Until other teleconnections are identified and better understood, predicting the weather a month or season ahead is a chancy proposition, given the atmosphere's chaotic behaviour.

Want another hot tip? Given the likelihood of a warmer planet due to global warming, try investing your money in Kapuskasing orchards, Maritime sea walls and Baffin beach resorts.

Quiz: How Weatherwise Are You?

If you're a Canadian, you've probably experienced more weather in one year than most people do in an entire lifetime. Consider yourself one of the most weather-astute, weather-conversant, weather-sensitive people around. From coast to coast, the weather, good or bad, is something all Canadians have in common. Also common among Canadians is our fascination with information trivia.

Here's a fun quiz that will show you exactly how absorbed Canadians can get with two of our favourite pastimes: the weather and trivia. Test your weather wisdom by taking this challenging weather quiz. In whole or in part, these fascinating weather-related trivia and factoids are guaranteed to entertain you and should make you a hit at your next social gathering.

Who knows—you may be a genuine weather weenie! Or even better, a supreme weather wizard!

1. The Montreal Expos made Major League history on July 1, 1974, when a game they were hosting at Jarry Park was delayed due to: (a) an earthquake; (b) a lightning strike; (c) glare from the sun; (d) heavy snowflurries; (e) baseball-size hail

2. Which of the following golfers has been struck by lightning? (a) Bobby Nichols; (b) Lee Trevino; (c) Seve Ballesteros; (d) Tony Jacklin; (e) all of the above

3. Which of the following travels slowest? (a) Brett Hull's slapshot; (b) Roger Clemens's fastball; (c) a hurricane; (d) tornado winds; (e) falling hailstones

4. What caused a baseball game indoors at Houston's Astrodome to be postponed on June 15, 1976? (a) rain; (b) earthquake; (c) heat and humidity; (d) tsunami warning; (e) bomb threat

5. Which is the least rainy city? (a) New York City; (b) Miami; (c) Seattle; (d) Boston; (e) Atlanta

6. If you want to avoid being hit by a hurricane, you should go to (a) Hawaii; (b) New Zealand; (c) the equator; (d) Vancouver Island; (e) North Sea

7. Which country has never launched a weather satellite? (a) Russia; (b) China; (c) India; (d) Japan; (e) Canada

8. What is wrong with this statement: last night the mercury fell to −45° Celsius at Winnipeg? (a) temperature doesn't really fall; (b) Winnipeg has never had a temperature below −45°; (c) with negative temperatures we say temperature rose above; (d) below −40° thermometers use alcohol; (e) metric scale is Centigrade not Celsius

9. Which continent has never had a hurricane? (a) Asia; (b) Africa; (c) Australia; (d) South America; (e) Antarctica

10. Which of the following killer events took the most number of lives, 243? (a) Hurricane Andrew; (b) Mississippi floods in 1994; (c) the East Coast blizzard in March 1993; (d) Hurricane Hugo; (e) eruption of Mount St. Helens.

11. The earth is closest to the sun on (a) September 21; (b) January 3; (c) March 21; (d) June 21; (e) July 3

12. In what 1942 movie did Bing Crosby initially refuse to sing a song that later became his biggest-selling record? (a) *Singin' in the Rain*; (b) *Going My Way*; (c) *Holiday Inn*; (d) *White Christmas*; (e) *Stormy Weather*

13. Jet-stream winds are a band of high-altitude winds that circle the globe. They were discovered (a) when weather satellites were first launched in 1957; (b) by American U2 pilot Gary Powers over the Soviet Union in 1960; (c) by a German Luftwaffe aircraft over the Mediterranean in 1938; (d) at the beginning of the 20th century from weather kites; (e) in 1783 when the first hot-air balloon to carry humans ascended

14. The Monroe phenomenon refers to winds that slide down buildings with smooth surfaces and bounce back off the pavement. It is named for: (a) wind engineer Charles Monroe; (b) Monroe, Michigan, where it was first detected; (c) Marilyn Monroe's problem with her skirts in *The Seven Year Itch*; (d) Monroe Towers in Manhattan, New York; (e) American president James Monroe

15. Which pole is colder? (a) the South Pole; (b) the North Pole.

16. Which body of water contributes more to snowfall in the Maritimes? (a) the Great Lakes; (b) the Gulf of Mexico; (c) Pacific Ocean; (d) Hudson Bay; (e) the Arctic Ocean; (f) Baffin Bay

17. How long does it take for a snowflake to reach the ground on its own from a height of 3 km? (a) 3 minutes; (b) ten minutes; (c) 30 minutes; (d) 2 hours; (e) 24 hours

18. Which of the following Canadian media personalities did not begin his or her career as a weather broadcaster? (a) CBC's Shelagh Rogers; (b) "Hockey Night in Canada"'s Ron McLean; (c) Mr. Dress-up, Ernie Coombs; (d) retired CBC broadcaster Knowlton Nash; (e) Judy Halliday of the Discovery Channel

19. Of the following locations, which is the safest during a lightning storm? (a) baseball diamond; (b) forest; (c) swimming pool; (d) telephone booth; (e) golf course

20. Who said, "The way I see it, if you want the rainbow, you've gotta put up with the rain"? (a) Art Linkletter; (b) Marshall McLuhan; (c) Boutros Boutros Ghali; (d) Dolly Parton; (e) The Artist formerly known as Prince

21. The macintosh was invented in 1823 by the Scottish chemist Charles Macintosh. He bound two layers of fabric with a solution of naphtha and Indian rubber. Early macintoshes were called: (a) umbrellas; (b) parkas; (c) souwesters; (d) galoshes; (e) raincoats

22. In the open ocean, a tsunami or high-energy wave moves at an incredible speed of up to 1,000 km/h. Ships may not even notice it, yet near shore it can create monster waves that cause enormous damage. What is their principal cause: (a) tidal wave; (b) hurricane; (c) under-sea earthquake; (d) landslide; (e) volcano

23. Where would you find the coldest weather? (a) Verkhoyansk, Siberia; (b) 15 km above the equator; (c) Snag, Yukon; (d) the South Pole; (e) the thermosphere, about 300 km above the earth's surface

24. Which day of the week do the biggest snowfalls occur in Winnipeg? This day has twice the number of occurrences of heavy snowfalls (greater than 10 cm) than any other: (a) Saturday; (b) Monday; (c) Tuesday; (d) Friday; (e) Sunday

25. What trees are the ones most likely to be struck by lightning? (a) fir; (b) oak; (c) beech; (d) pine; (e) maple

26. Which of the following locations gets the least rain? (a) central Sahara; (b) Death Valley, California; (c) northern Chile; (d) Eureka, N.W.T.; (e) Antarctica

27. The peak month for tornadoes in the United States is May, and in Canada it is June and July. On average, Great Britain gets about

40 or 50 tornadoes each year. What is the peak month for British twisters? (a) July; (b) June; (c) August; (d) April; (e) October

28. In campaigns to lure immigrants to the Canadian West, the Canadian government forbade the use of this word in official brochures and handouts in Europe: (a) frontier; (b) communism; (c) cold; (d) mosquitoes; (e) floods; (f) cyclone

29. Under certain weather conditions, at which of these airports is the roar of jetliners so loud during and after takeoff that officials must close the airport? (a) Edmonton; (b) Phoenix; (c) Washington; (d) Montreal; (e) Chicago

30. In a recent survey of their views on the environment, especially climate change, residents of which city were more likely to favour limiting car use? (a) Montreal; (b) Toronto; (c) Winnipeg; (d) Halifax; (e) Vancouver

31. In which month did both the hottest and coldest temperatures ever recorded on the surface of the earth occur? The two temperature extremes spanned almost 150°C. (a) May; (b) July; (c) September; (d) June; (e) January

32. Amenomania is a disease that causes victims to become: (a) concerned with the nutritional value of their food; (b) morbidly anxious about the direction of the wind; (c) lethargic from an excess of positive air ions; (d) depressed by long bouts of static weather; (e) worried over distant light flickering

33. Operation Desert Storm, the UN-coalition effort to liberate Kuwait, occurred in 1991. What was Operation Typhoon? (a) U.S. air strikes into North Vietnam in 1965; (b) German attempt to capture Moscow in 1941; (c) code for Canadian operations in the Pacific front at the close of World War II; (d) U.S. push to re-take Seoul during the Korean War; (e) Chinese military manoeuvres around Taipei in 1996

34. To South American gauchos, the word *el tormento* refers to what weather term? (a) blizzard; (b) sandstorm; (c) drizzly fog; (d) wind chill; (e) dust devil

35. The westerlies is a belt of stormy latitudes. Sailors in the North Atlantic named them: (a) the whirling westerlies; (b) horse latitudes; (c) Screaming Fifties; (d) the trades; (e) Roaring Forties

36. An ombrometre and a micropluviometre are technical words for what weather instrument? (a) rain gauge; (b) cloud-height sensor; (c) satellite cloud camera; (d) miniature soil moisture instruments; (e) acid snow gauge

37. Recently, green elves have been discovered in the atmosphere. Are they (a) lightning that occurs high above clouds on the fringes of space; (b) air ions that are gradually filling in the ozone hole; (c) visible cloud streaks just ahead of a severe thunderstorm; (d) contrails from small jetliners; (e) plumes spotted by astronauts above the Amazon rain forest; (f) daytime afterglow from Northern Lights?

38. What kills more people in North America each year? (a) earthquakes; (b) avalanches; (c) hang gliding; (d) hurricanes; (e) bee stings

39. In meteorology, what does the word *serein* mean? (a) black ice that forms out of the exhaust from tailpipes; (b) snow or rain falling from a clear sky; (c) a warm comforting breeze; (d) perfect rainbow that occurs from falling snow; (e) green flash at sunset

40. Isobar refers to a line on a weather chart connecting points that have the same value of atmospheric pressure; isotherms refer to equal air pressure. Isobronts are lines of equal (a) time of some occurrence, such as a wind shift; (b) frequency of observing aurora borealis; (c) number of hailstorm events; (d) amount of thunder; (e) depth in water having same temperature

41. Black rail refers to: (a) slippery streetcar tracks at temperatures near freezing; (b) name of the oldest meteorological station in England; (c) ice that forms on roadways from automobile exhaust; (d) the blackened centre in solar radiation instruments; (e) abandoned railway line

42. What are hypercanes? (a) hurricanes whose maximum wind speed exceed 250 km/h; (b) hurricanes that cross the International Date Line changing from hurricane to typhoon or vice versa; (c) theoretical superstrong hurricanes whose winds exceed 1,000 km/h; (d) hurricanes that kill more than 1,000 people or damage property in excess of $1 billion

43. Potentially, the greatest hazard to scientists chasing severe thunderstorms are: (a) large hail; (b) damaging winds; (c) tornado hidden behind rain; (d) highway traffic; (e) fallen trees and powerlines; (f) lightning

44. What U.S. state has the most golfers per capita? (a) Florida; (b) California; (c) Arizona; (d) North Dakota; (e) South Carolina

45. Which of the following is not the name of a famous physicist whose name applies to measures of temperature? (a) Fahrenheit; (b) Centigrade; (c) Reaumur; (d) Celsius; (e) Kelvin

46. What is a wind rose? (a) an Arctic flower; (b) a diagram of proportional directions; (c) name of instrument to measure wind speed; (d) gentle wind stronger than a calm but lighter than a breeze; (e) Beaufort force 2

47. In Canada, which month has the greatest average number of tornadoes a year? (a) April; (b) May; (c) June; (d) July; (e) August

48. Which province is the leading consumer, per capita, of ice cream? (a) Prince Edward Island; (b) Quebec; (c) Manitoba; (d) British Columbia; (e) Ontario

49. Which is the driest continent? (a) Asia; (b) Africa; (c) Australia; (d) North America; (e) Antarctic

50. Niphablepsia is what form of weather malady? (a) snowblindness; (b) frostbite; (c) weather migraine; (d) prickly heat

51. Yellow snow is: (a) caused by the presence in it of pine or cypress pollen; (b) piled at the end of driveways; (c) found only in the mountains of the Sahara Desert; (d) synthetic snow; (e) manmade snow

52. Which is the snowiest major city in Canada? (a) Winnipeg; (b) Moncton; (c) St. John's; (d) Montreal; (e) Quebec City

53. If one considers heat, cold, flood, drought, tornadoes and tropical storms, which country has the worst weather on earth? (a) Bangladesh; (b) Canada; (c) United States; (d) China; (e) Australia

54. The irrational fear of thunder is termed: (a) keraunophobia; (b) katathunphobia; (c) cumulonimbusphobia; (d) brontophobia; (e) sphericphobia

55. What shape are raindrops? (a) teardrops; (b) pear shape; (c) six-sided crystal; (d) round; (e) hamburger bun

56. What weather phenomenon kills more people in the developed world than any other natural phenomenon? (a) lightning; (b) drought; (c) hurricanes; (d) tornadoes; (e) floods

57. What temperature does pure alcohol freeze at? (a) −39°C; (b) −81°C; (c) −100°C; (d) −115°C; (e) −273°C

58. What place has more rainbows than any other location in the world? (a) Singapore; (b) Tampa; (c) Glasgow; (d) Honolulu; (e) Katmandu

59. Which of these weather phenomena are classical music composers most likely to capture in their scores? (a) wind; (b) summer heat; (c) thunderstorms; (d) mist and fog; (e) clouds

60. If the temperature outside today is 0°C, and the forecast for tomorrow is for "twice as cold," how cold will it be? (a) –1°C; (b) –10°C; (c) –32°C; (d) –50°C; (e) –137°C

61. Which of these American cities is the windiest? (a) New York; (b) Boston; (c) Chicago; (d) Phoenix; (e) Dallas

62. Which city has the greatest number of hours of blowing snow? (a) Regina; (b) Charlottetown; (c) Windsor; (d) St. John's; (e) Winnipeg

63. Which city is the sunniest in winter? (a) Winnipeg; (b) Estevan; (c) Calgary; (d) Thunder Bay; (e) Halifax

64. Which month is Hudson Bay free of ice? (a) July; (b) August; (c) September; (d) October; (e) November

65. To weather experts, a "very cold day" in Canada is considered to be: (a) 0°C; (b) –7°C; (c) –10°C; (d) –18°C; (e) –40°C

66. How many snowflakes fall on Canada in one year? (a) equal to the number of cents in the national deficit; (b) 10 million (1 plus 6 zeros); (c) 100 kazillion (indefinite number of zeros); (d) 1 septillion (1 plus 24 zeros); (e) sexdecillion (1 plus 51 zeros)

67. A zephyr is: (a) the Greek goddess of weather; (b) Admiral Beaufort's description of a 30 km/h wind; (c) a gentle breeze; (d) a town in the Yukon; (e) a snow ruler

68. Spring in Quebec begins when: (a) the snow disappears; (b) the Canadiens' hockey season ends; (c) the ice on the St. Lawrence disappears; (d) the maple sap flows; (e) the first thunder is heard

69. Which capital holds western Canada's one-day snowfall record?
(a) Edmonton; (b) Victoria; (c) Regina; (d) Winnipeg; (e)
Whitehorse

70. Canada holds the world weather record for which of the following? (a) the most snow in one year; (b) the lowest temperature;
(c) the highest wind speed; (d) the lowest rainfall; (e) none of the
above

71. Which place in Canada has the largest number of sunny days a
year? (a) Kamloops; (b) Toronto; (c) Calgary; (d) Fredericton;
(e) Sunshine, B.C.

72. What is a weather bomb? (a) an erroneous forecast; (b) a sudden
explosive marine storm; (c) a mushroom-shaped cloud; (d) a loud
clap of thunder without the accompanying lightning; (e) a dry
tornado

73. Which of the following moves the fastest? (a) snowflakes in a blizzard; (b) a hurricane; (c) a large hailstone; (d) the winner of the
Queen's Plate; (e) ice pellets

74. If climate changes occur as climatologists predict, the climate of
Vancouver in 2100 will resemble which city today? (a) Prince
Rupert; (b) Victoria; (c) Seattle; (d) Toronto; (e) San Francisco

75. In Newfoundland, a growler is: (a) a small iceberg; (b) a moose in
heat; (c) a boss with a short temper; (d) an empty cod net; (e) a
strong gust of wind

76. In Nova Scotia, a fungy is: (a) a fish stew; (b) a foggy-windy day;
(c) an old, unseaworthy boat; (d) a deep blueberry pie; (e) a day
with freezing rain

77. Which of the following is true? (a) pets feel the wind chill; (b) you
only feel the wind chill under a high-pressure system; (c) the wind

chill is always lower when the sun is shining; (d) in a calm the wind chill is lower than the air temperature

78. Of the following, who did not begin his or her career as a weathercaster? (a) Suzanne Sommers; (b) David Letterman; (c) Pat Sajak; (d) Diane Sawyer; (e) Danny De Vito

79. Which cloud is often mistaken for a UFO? (a) altocumulus lenticularis; (b) scud; (c) roll cloud; (d) cumulus congestus; (e) cap cloud or pileus cloud

80. Fata Morgana is: (a) a mirage; (b) headquarters of the Italian weather service; (c) a tropical storm made famous by having shipwrecked Henry Morgan; (d) inventor of the barometer; (e) lightning that strikes the top of a mast

81. Most victims struck and killed by lightning die because of: (a) heart attack; (b) third-degree skin burns; (c) suffocation; (d) exploded intestines; (e) charred blood vessels

82. Residents of which province are least likely to report personal health problems brought on by weather? (a) Ontario; (b) Quebec; (c) Newfoundland; (d) British Columbia; (e) Saskatchewan

83. Which name has been called into use most often for North Atlantic hurricanes? (a) Anna/Ana; (b) Arlene; (c) Debbie/Debby; (d) Edith; (e) Florence

84. What is the only Canadian city to make the list of the top 10 coldest inhabited places in the world? (a) Winnipeg; (b) Thompson; (c) Whitehorse; (d) Yellowknife; (e) Iqaluit

85. What is the safest place to be during a tornado? (a) bathroom; (b) bedroom; (c) kitchen; (d) front porch or balcony; (e) a car

86. Which country has the highest participation rate for golf in the world? (a) United States; (b) Scotland; (c) Switzerland; (d) Canada; (e) Japan

87. Who said, "Everybody talks about the weather, but nobody does anything about it"? (a) Benjamin Franklin; (b) Charles Warner; (c) Samuel Clemens; (d) Abraham Lincoln; (e) Johnny Carson

88. From what vocation are most volunteer weather observers recruited? (a) public servants; (b) teachers; (c) housewives; (d) farmers; (e) meteorologists

89. What do Yoyo, Manyberries and Goobies have in common? (a) Canadian weather stations; (b) birthplaces of Canadian prime ministers; (c) names of ocean weather ships; (d) what Peppermint Patty calls clouds; (e) red rocks on Mars

90. Fairy squall, dwye and sheila's brush/blush are: (a) stages in the life cycle of a tornado; (b) Newfoundland winds; (c) reggae words for hurricane; (d) dust storms on the Australian outback; (e) other names for heat, sheet and streak lightning

91. Willy-willies were once hurricanes. Now they are: (a) the Korean name for a blizzard; (b) an Australian dust devil or whirlwind; (c) a wet bathing suit contest; (d) a local Scottish term for cold waves; (e) what Californians call snow flurries

92. Which American president was also a weather observer: (a) Ben Franklin; (b) John Kennedy; (c) George Washington; (d) U.S. Grant; (e) Richard Nixon

93. In the 10 years following the Edmonton tornado on July 31, 1987, how many people have been killed by tornadoes in Canada? (a) none; (b) 13; (c) 25; (d) 30; (e) 80

94. The first regular weather observations in Canada were taken by:
    (a) farmers; (b) meteorologists; (c) telegraph operators; (d) trappers; (e) surgeons

95. When over 400,000 of Napoleon's troops died in the Russian cold, the greatest losses were among those who were: (a) over six feet; (b) bald; (c) native to the south coast of France; (d) front-line soldiers; (e) without guns

96. In 1803 Luke Howard, an English weather hobbyist, devised a scheme for classifying cloud types into cirrus, cumulus and stratus. What was Howard's occupation: (a) Latin professor; (b) artist; (c) druggist; (d) ship captain; (e) shepherd

97. What is the average lifetime (in days) of an Atlantic hurricane?
    (a) 3; (b) 9; (c) 13; (d) 24; (e) 30

98. Which Canadian province receives the most precipitation annually? (a) Newfoundland-Labrador; (b) Quebec; (c) Nova Scotia; (d) Ontario; (e) British Columbia

99. According to the *Reader's Digest*, the snowiest city in North America is found in: (a) Alberta; (b) California; (c) British Columbia; (d) Alaska; (e) Quebec

100. Which of the following cities gets the least amount of rain during an average year: (a) Berlin; (b) Paris; (c) Lisbon; (d) London; (e) Vienna

RESULTS

Scoring 0 to 25—More of a *WEATHER WIMP* than a weather weenie. Don't go around criticizing weather forecasters. You need help, but all is not lost! Don't be discouraged—take time to watch the weather, and you'll be surprised what you can learn.

Scoring 25 to 50—Good! You're a *WEATHER WIT*—showing great potential, but there's room for improvement. Just a little more effort will make you a weather weenie. Be sure to watch the skies and listen for interesting weather information.

Scoring 51 to 75—Congratulations! You are very well informed on weather and related trivia. Consider yourself a *WEATHER WEENIE*— it's a great honour!

Scoring 76 to 100—Hail, *WEATHER WIZARD*! You've reached the pinnacle of weather triviadom! You have the right to criticize weather experts.

ANSWERS

1.	c	26.	e	51.	a	76.	d
2.	e	27.	e	52.	b	77.	a
3.	c	28.	c	53.	c	78.	e
4.	a	29.	b	54.	d	79.	a
5.	c	30.	e	55.	e	80.	a
6.	c	31.	b	56.	a	81.	c
7.	e	32.	b	57.	d	82.	b
8.	d	33.	b	58.	d	83.	b
9.	e	34.	a	59.	c	84.	d
10.	c	35.	e	60.	e	85.	a
11.	b	36.	a	61.	b	86.	d
12.	c	37.	a	62.	a	87.	b
13.	c	38.	e	63.	a	88.	d
14.	c	39.	b	64.	c	89.	a
15.	a	40.	d	65.	d	90.	b
16.	b	41.	a	66.	d	91.	b
17.	c	42.	c	67.	c	92.	c
18.	c	43.	d	68.	d	93.	a
19.	b	44.	d	69.	b	94.	e
20.	d	45.	b	70.	e	95.	b
21.	a	46.	b	71.	c	96.	c
22.	c	47.	c	72.	b	97.	b
23.	b	48.	c	73.	c	98.	a
24.	b	49.	e	74.	e	99.	b
25.	b	50.	a	75.	a	100.	d

 Glossary

air mass: an extensive body of air with a fairly uniform distribution of moisture and temperature throughout

atmosphere: the envelope of air surrounding the earth; most weather events are confined to the lower 10 km of the atmosphere

atmospheric pressure: the force exerted on the earth by the weight of the atmosphere

blizzard: severe winter weather condition characterized by low temperatures, strong winds above 40 km/h and visibility of less than 1 km due to blowing snow; condition lasts three hours or more

blowing snow: snow lifted from the earth's surface by the wind to a height of two metres or more; blowing snow rises higher than drifting snow

bright sunshine: sunshine intense enough to burn a mark on recording paper mounted in the Campbell-Stokes sunshine recorder; the daily period of bright sunshine is less than that of visible sunshine because the sun's rays are not intense enough to burn the paper just after sunrise, near sunset and under cloudy conditions

chinook (snow-eater): a dry, warm, strong wind that blows down the eastern slopes of the Rocky Mountains in North America; the warmth and dryness are due principally to heating by compression as the air descends the mountain slope

climate: the long-term average that describes what kind of weather can be expected

cold wave: an occurrence of dangerous cold conditions, when temperatures often dip below −18°C, that usually lasts longer than a few days

crepuscular rays: rays caused by streaks or beams of sunlight shining through openings in large cumulonimbus clouds on the horizon; the beams reach down and outward from behind the clouds; if they focus upward, towards a point in the sky opposite the sun, they are called anti-crepuscular rays; sometimes they are called sunbeams, crossing the sky, or Jacob's ladder; sailors refer to them as "the sun drawing water"; the dark bands seen crossing the sky are the shadows from clouds

cyclone: a generic term that describes all classes of storms from local thunderstorms and tiny dust devils to monstrous hurricanes and typhoons; it comes from the Greek word, *kyllon*, meaning "eyele," "circle" or "coil of a snake" and refers to all circular wind systems

deep low: used to describe the central barometric pressure of a low, usually when it is about 975 millibars (97.50 kPa or less); often has winds of gale to storm force around the low

developing low: a low in which the central barometric pressure is decreasing with time (winds would normally increase as the low deepens)

dew-point temperature: the temperature at which air becomes saturated, allowing condensation of water vapour as frost, fog, dew, mist or precipitation

drizzle: precipitation consisting of numerous minute water droplets that appear to float; the droplets are much smaller than in rain

El Niño: Near the end of most years, the normally cold Peru Current, which sweeps northward along the South American coast from southern Chile to the equator, is replaced by a warm southward flowing coastal current; centuries ago the local fishermen named this the Christ child current because it appeared around the Christmas season; every few years it was unusually intense and over time the term *El Niño* became more closely associated with occasional intense warmings

filling low: a low in which the central barometric pressure is increasing with time, i.e., the low is gradually weakening

flash floods: a very rapid rise of water with little or no advance warning, most often when an intense thunderstorm drops a huge rainfall on a fairly small area in a very short time

fog: a cloud based at the earth's surface consisting of tiny water droplets or, under very cold conditions, ice crystals or ice fog; generally found in calm or low wind conditions; under foggy conditions, visibility is reduced to less than 1 km

frazil ice: during the freeze-up period, ice forms on a river surface and ice crystals or frazil develop within the river, especially in open turbulent water slightly below 0°C; frazil ice is very common in rapids

freezing precipitation: supercooled water drops of drizzle or rain that freeze on impact to form a coating of ice on the ground or on any objects they strike

front: the boundary between two different air masses that have originated from widely separated regions; a cold front is the leading edge of an advancing cold-air mass, and a warm front is the trailing edge of a retreating cold-air mass

frost: the deposit of ice crystals that occurs when the air temperature is at or below the freezing point of water; the term *frost* is also used to describe the icy deposits of water vapour that may form on the ground or on other surfaces like car windshields; these are colder than the surrounding air and have a temperature below freezing

gale: a strong wind; a gale warning is issued for expected winds of 65 to 100 km/h *gust:* a sudden, brief increase in wind speed, for generally less than 20 seconds

heat wave: a period with more than three consecutive days of maximum temperatures at or above 32°C

high pressure: a term for an area of high (maximum) pressure with a closed, clockwise (in the Northern Hemisphere) circulation of air

humidex: a measure of what hot weather "feels like"; air of a given temperature and moisture content is equated in comfort to air with a higher temperature and negligible moisture content; at a humidex of 30°C some people begin to experience discomfort.

hurricanes: tropical systems are classed into several categories, depending on maximum strength, usually measured by maximum sustained wind speed; a tropical disturbance is simply a moving area of thunderstorms in the tropics that maintains its identity for 24 hours or more; a tropical depression is a cyclonic system originating over the tropics with a highest sustained wind speed of up to 61 km/h; a tropical storm has a highest sustained wind speed of between 62 and 117 km/h; a hurricane has wind speeds of 118 km/h or more

ice fog (ice-crystal fog, frozen fog, frost fog, frost flakes, rime fog, pogonip): a type of fog composed of suspended particles of ice that occurs at very low temperatures (below –35°C), and usually in clear, calm weather in high latitudes; the sun is usually visible and may cause halos; it is almost always present at air temperatures of –45°C in the vicinity of a source of water vapour, such as fast-flowing streams, herds of animals and products of combustion for heating or propulsion

ice pellets: precipitation consisting of fragments of ice, 5 mm or less in diameter, that bounce when hitting a hard surface, making a sound on impact

inversion: a temperature increase with altitude, whereas the usual pattern is a decrease in temperature with altitude

isobar: a line on a weather map or chart connecting points of equal pressure; the large concentric lines on television or newspaper weather maps are isobars

killing frost: a frost severe enough to end the growing season, usually when the air temperature falls below $-2°C$

land breeze: a small-scale wind set off when the air temperature over water is warmer than that over adjacent land; a land breeze develops at night and blows from the land out to the sea or onto a lake; its counterpart is the sea or lake breeze

low pressure: an area of low (minimum) atmospheric pressure that has a closed counterclockwise circulation in the Northern Hemisphere

peak wind (gust): the highest instantaneous wind speed recorded for a specific time period

plough winds: these belong to a family of strong, straight-line downburst winds found in thunderstorms; they rush to the ground with great force, maybe 100 to 150 km/h and occasionally even higher; damage usually covers an area less than 3 km across; plough winds are capable of toppling trees, lifting roofs and ripping apart houses and other structures

precipitation: any and all forms of water, whether liquid or solid, that fall from the atmosphere and reach the earth's surface; a day with measurable precipitation is a day when the water equivalent of the precipitation is equal to or greater than 0.2 mm

probability of precipitation (POP): a subjective numerical estimate of the chance of measurable precipitation at some time during the forecast period; for example, a 40 percent probability of rain means there are 4 chances in 10 of getting wet; it cannot be used to predict when, where or how much precipitation will occur

relative humidity: the ratio of water vapour in the air at a given temperature to the maximum that could exist at that temperature; it is usually expressed as a percentage

ridge: an elongated area of high pressure extending from the centre of a high-pressure region; the opposite of a trough

sea breeze: a small-scale wind set off when the air temperature over land is greater than that over the adjacent sea; a sea breeze develops during the day and blows from the sea to the land; its counterpart is the land breeze

sleet: in the United States, sleet is frozen raindrops that bounce when they hit the surface; it is not as treacherous to drive on as is freezing rain; what Americans call sleet a Canadian would call ice pellets or frozen raindrops, spherical or irregular shapes with a diameter of 5 mm or less; pellets do not stick to trees or wires; sleet to a British weather watcher is a mix of rain and partly melted snowflakes

small-craft warning: issued when winds over coastal marine areas are expected to reach and maintain speeds of 20 to 33 knots

snow: precipitation consisting of white or translucent ice crystals, often agglomerated into snowflakes; a day with measurable snow is a day when the total snowfall is at least 0.2 cm

squall: a strong, sudden wind that generally lasts a few minutes, then quickly decreases in speed; squalls are generally associated with severe thunderstorms

storm track: the path taken by a low-pressure centre

storm warning: the wind warning that is issued to mariners when winds are expected to be 48 to 63 knots

thunderstorm: a local storm, usually produced by a cumulonimbus cloud, and always accompanied by thunder and lightning; a thunderstorm day is a day when thunder is heard or when lightning is seen (rain and snow need not have fallen)

tidal wave: any unusually high and destructive water level along a shore; also called a storm surge

tornado (twister): a violently rotating column of air that is usually visible as a funnel cloud hanging from dark thunderstorm clouds; one of the least extensive of all storms, but in violence the most destructive

trough: an elongated area of low pressure extending from the centre of a low pressure region; the opposite of a ridge

tsunami: also known (incorrectly) as a tidal wave; "*tsunami*" is the Japanese word for "harbour wave"; it is a wave set in motion by an undersea movement such as an earthquake or a landslide; these waves can travel up to 1,000 km/hr over long distances, hitting the shore with tremendous force

typhoon: a severe tropical cyclone in the western Pacific Ocean; the counterpart of the Atlantic hurricane

virga: streaks of falling rain that evaporate before reaching the ground

watches and warnings: Environment Canada alerts Canadians to severe storms by issuing weather watches and warnings; usually the first message is the severe thunderstorm watch; if a watch is issued in your area, maintain your normal routine, but keep an eye skyward for threatening weather, and listen to radio and television for further weather information; when severe local storms are building, or have actually been sighted or detected by radar, then warnings are issued and updated; these may be either severe thunderstorm warnings or tornado warnings; warnings mean you should be on the alert

waterspout: often called a tornado over water, the actual water spray involved does not extend from the surface to the cloud, but 3 to 10 m above the water surface; like the tornado, the waterspout is very brief; sailors believed one way of breaking up a waterspout was to fire a cannon through it

westerlies (west-wind belt): the pronounced west-to-east motion of the atmosphere centred over middle latitudes from about 35 to 65 degrees latitude

willy-willies: small, circular winds such as dust devils or whirlwinds in Australia, not very hazardous; before 1950, willy-willies referred to much larger, more destructive typhoons or hurricanes

wind chill: a simple measure of the chilling effect experienced by the human body when strong winds are combined with freezing temperatures; the larger the wind chill, the faster the rate of cooling; the wind chill factor is expressed in watts per square metre or in °C (an equivalent temperature)

wind direction: the direction from which the wind is blowing

Bibliography

Bangs, Cameron, and Murray P. Hamlet. "Hypothermia and Cold Injuries." In: *Management of Wilderness and Environmental Emergencies.* New York: Macmillan Publishing Co., 1983, 27-63.

Bangs, Cameron, John Boswick, Murray Hamlet, David Summer and R.C.A. Weatherley-White. "When Your Patient Suffers Frostbite." *Patient Care*, February 1, 1977, 132-157.

Barrie, Leonard A. "Arctic Air Pollution: An Overview of Current Knowledge." *Atmospheric Environment*, 1986, 643-663.

Bear, I.J., and Z.H. Kranz. "Fatty Acids from Exposed Rock Surfaces." *Australian Journal of Chemistry*, 1965, 915-917.

Benson, Carl S. "Ice Fog: Low Temperature Air Pollution." *University of Alaska, Geophysical Institute*, UAG R-173, 1965.

Burroughs, William J., Bob Crowder, Ted Robertson, Eleanor Vallier-Talbot and Richard Whitaker. *Weather.* The Nature Company Guides. Time-Life Books, 1996.

Chelminski, Rudolph. "Coldest Village in The World." *The Atlantic Monthly*, October 1977.

Clary, Mike. "Chasing Tornadoes." *Weatherwise*, June 1986, 136-145.

Court, Arnold, Norman Sissenwine and George S. Mitchell. "Lowest Temperatures in the Northern Hemisphere." *Weatherwise*, February 1949, 10-11, 22.

Dennis, Jerry, and Glenn Wolff. *It's Raining Frogs and Fishes.* New York: Harper/Collins Publishers, 1992.

Environment Canada. "The Impact of Storm '96 on Environmental, Social and Economic Conditions." *Atmospheric Environment Program,* February 1997.

Freier, George D. *Weather Proverbs.* Tucson, Arizona: Fisher Books, 1992.

Garelik, Glenn. "The Weather Peddlers." *Discover,* April 1985, 18-24.

Getler, Warren. "Some Meteorologists Reap Windfall from Crop Futures Markets." *The Wall Street Journal,* July 13, 1993.

Goold, Douglas. "Whither Weather and the Markets." *The Globe and Mail,* March 14, 1996.

Greenler, Robert G., Monte Drinkwine, A. James Mallmann and George Blumenthal. "The Origin of Sun Pillars." *American Scientist,* May-June 1972, 292-302.

Gribben, John. "Do Volcanoes Affect the Climate?" *New Scientist,* January 1982, 150-153.

Hauptman, William. "On the Dryline." *The Atlantic Monthly,* May 1984, 76-87.

Hornstein, R.A. "Snow Rollers." *Weather,* June 1951, 168-169.

Long, Marion. "The Man Who Chases Tornadoes." *Science Digest,* May 1984, 5 pp.

Lyons, Walter A. *The Handy Weather Answer Book.* Detroit: Visible Ink Press, 1997.

Mallmann, James. "Halos, Rings, and Arcs in the Sky." *Astronomy*, April 1979, 42-46.

Marshall, Tim. *Storm Chase Manual.* Lewisville, Texas: Stormtracker, 1-62.

Masterton, J.M., and F.A. Richardson. "Humidex." Environment Canada, *Atmospheric Environment Service CLI 1-79*, 1979.

Morrow, Lance. "The Wonderful Art of Weathercasting." *Time*, March 17, 1980.

Moss, Stephen, and Paul Simons. *Weather Watch.* London: BBC Books, 1992.

Newark, Mike. *Tornado History Project.* Atmospheric Environment Service, (personal communication), 1992.

Niederman, Derrick. *This Is Not Your Father's Stockpicking Book.* New York: Time Business Books, 1995.

Ohtake, Takeshi. "Studies of Ice Fog." *University of Alaska, Geophysical Institute Final Report AP-00449*, June 1970.

Pankratz, Allen. "Snow Rollers." *Chinook*, Fall 1985, 54-55.

Phillips, D.W., and R.B. Crowe. "Climate Severity Index for Canadians." Environment Canada, *Atmospheric Environment Service CLI 1-84*, 1984.

Quayle, Robert, and Fred Doehring. "Heat Stress." *Weatherwise*, June 1981, 120-124.

Quine, Chris, Mike Coutts, Barry Gardiner and Graham Pyatt. "Forests and Wind: Management to Minimise Damage." *The Forestry Authority*, Forestry Commission Bulletin 114, 1995.

Rahn, Kenneth A. "Who's Polluting the Arctic?" *Natural History*, May 1984, 30-38.

Riley, Frank. "A Snowball's Chance." *New Scientist*, January 14, 1988.

Rosen, Jay. "Don't Need a Weatherman?" *Harper's Magazine*, April 1989, 34-36.

Saunders, Edward M. "Stock Prices and Wall Street Weather." *American Economic Review*, December 1993, 1337-1345.

Soroos, Marvin S. "The Odyssey of Arctic Haze." *Environment*, December 1992, 6-27.

Stathers, R.J., T.P. Rollerson and S.J. Mitchell. "Windthrow Handbook for British Columbia Forests." BC Ministry of Forests, *Working Paper 9401*, 1994.

Thomas, Morley. *The Beginnings of Canadian Meteorology*. Toronto: ECW Press, 1991.

Thomas, Morley. "A Brief History of Meteorological Services in Canada" (three parts). *Atmosphere*, 1971, 3-15; 37-47; 69-79.

Thomas, Morley. *Forecasts for Flying*. Toronto: ECW Press, 1996.

Toon, O.B., and J.B. Pollack. "Atmospheric Aerosols and Climate." *American Science*, 1980, 268-278.

Verkaik, Arjen, and Jerrine Verkaik. *Under the Whirlwind*. Elmwood, ON: Whirlwind Books, 1997.

Warkentin, A.A. "The Red River Flood of 1997." *CMOS Bulletin*, October 1997, 128-135.

Weatherwise magazine, Heldref Publications, Washington, DC.

Williams, Jack. *The Weather Book*. New York: Vintage Books, 1992.

World Meteorological Organization. "Meteorology and The Media." *WMO - No. 688*, 1987.

Index